PIG I‹

Nicholas Fisk has h   ...erent
occupations. He's served in the RAF, and been an
actor in an Irish Shakespeare company, a book
editor, a jazz musician, a journalist, worked in
advertising and as a freelance publishing con-
sultant. He's now a highly successful author with
well over forty books to his credit, as well as several
television scripts.

Described by *Twentieth Century Children's Writers*
as "the Huxley-Wyndham-Golding of children's
literature", Nicholas Fisk is particularly well-
known for his science-fiction stories. These include
Grinny; *A Rag, A Bone, and a Hank of Hair*; *Time
Trap;* and the Walker titles *Backlash* and *A Hole in
the Head* (shortlisted for the 1992 Earthworm
Award). He is also the author of the thriller *The
Worm Charmers* and stories for younger readers,
such as *Broops! Down the Chimney* and the picture
book, *The Model Village*.

Nicholas Fisk is married with four children and
lives in Hertfordshire.

Other books in the
Teenage Memoirs Series

Ordinary Seaman
by John Gordon

Smokestack Lightning
by Laurence Staig

Yesterday
by Adèle Geras

PIG
IGNORANT

NICHOLAS FISK

WALKER BOOKS
LONDON

First published 1992 by Walker Books Ltd
87 Vauxhall Walk, London SE11 5HJ

This edition published 1993

© 1992 Nicholas Fisk

Printed in England by Clays Ltd., St. Ives plc.

British Library Cataloguing in Publication Data
A catalogue record for this book is
available from the British Library.

ISBN 0-7445-2351-6

"I believe we all have a certain time in our lives that we're good at. I wasn't good at being a child."
Victoria Wood, comedienne

"If only a man knew how to choose among what he calls his experiences that which is really experience; and how to record truth truly."
Ralph Waldo Emerson, writer

ONE

Here he comes! Walking towards us! I see him distinctly, clear as day!— No, wait. That's not true. I don't see him distinctly at all. *What we are looking at is a walking, talking, breathing, solid ghost. Not the ghost of someone dead: I am still alive. His flesh is my flesh, his heartbeat is my heartbeat.*

Because he is me. But so long ago...

MUVVER'S DARLING

He's sixteen and a half. He is about six feet tall, fair-haired, ginger-jacketed, grey-trousered, pink-faced. He parts his hair right over on one side, which gives him a schoolboyish look. He bites his nails but will soon give up *that* schoolboy habit. For Nick, school is over! He's free! He's his real self at last!

Where is he? On the pavement of a middle-class London suburb. There are big, solid, Victorian houses on either side of the road. The front doors have stained-glass picture panes, solid brass door-knockers, glossy coats of dark paint.

The house that is his home has three and a half storeys of big rooms; and a full-size cellar. The whole tree-lined street is full of houses just like his, occupied by single families or even by a pair of old ladies like the Misses Albery next door.

These houses still stand but now they are split up into flats and flatlets. The once almost-empty street is today lined, bumper to bumper, with cars.

Correction: not all these houses still stand. One was knocked out like a tooth. We will come to that later, when Britain's Prime Minister, Neville Chamberlain, bleats his Declaration of War; when Herr Hitler shrieks his defiance; when, night after night, the air-raid sirens wail and hoot like gibbons; and the full-size cellars come into their own.

A car is stopping outside No. 44, where his friend Peter lives. A Sunbeam saloon with a fawn body, black wings and a golden polished-brass radiator. Lucky old Peter, having a Pa with a car. Not many people have cars. The streets belong to errand boys, cats and dogs, horse-drawn milk floats, lorries delivering Corona soft drinks, postmen with conical hats peaked in front and behind, and "Wallsie" the Walls Ice-Cream man pedalling his freezer-box trike.

Wait! Suddenly Nick looks a little different. His shoulders are taut and hunched, his face is pinker, his footsteps seem to have a slight swaggering, "don't-care" swing.

Why? There's that gang of whistling errand boys − four of them, doing circles on their heavy basket-carrying bikes. Nick's had trouble with errand boys. Errand boys gang up on you. You're riding your priceless, precious lightweight bike − Dunlop Sprite tyres, Simplex derailleur, three-speed gear, dropped handlebars, rat-trap pedals; and all at once there they are, the whistling errand boys, several of them, with their bikes blocking the road and their mouths grinning and their dirty teeth showing.

"'Ere, that's a noice boike! How much it corsst? Yer muvver buy it for yer?"

"Gotta lovely muvver, 'aven't chew? Fur coat an' all. No. 38, we seen 'er."

"Gotta lovely sister, too. Gor...!"

The fat, worn tyres of their front wheels butt against the delicate, shiny front wheel of your lightweight. A dirty hand locks on to your clean handlebars. No escape.

"Yerr, real noice boike for a real noice boy. Muvver's boy!"

"Yerr, proper little muvver's darling! Real muvver's boy!"

But that happened years and years ago, when he was twelve or thirteen. Just a kid. He's not a kid any more. I mean, just look at him! That sports coat, those polished shoes with toe caps. And that pipe in his jacket pocket. A pipe, and an ounce of Players Navy Mixture! He gave up fags months ago. Christine said, "I can't *stand* men smoking *ciggies*, they look sort of *nancy*. I mean, pipes, that's different. I like a man who smokes a pipe." So he bought a pipe. Because of Christine. Christine Endersleigh.

A PAIR OF COCONUTS

Christine! She's closing No. 35's front door, *her* front door! She's reached the gate! She's opening it!

If she turns left, she'll be walking away from him, she won't see him. Please God, let her turn left!

If she turns right, she'll come towards him, she'll see him, she'll smile and say "Oh, hello!" and he'll go bright red. All the same – please God, let her turn right!

She *has* turned right. And she *is* smiling, and saying "Oh, hello!" He can feel his face flaming and his mouth drying. But he plays it cool. One hand goes into his jacket pocket to clasp the briar pipe. She likes a man who smokes a pipe. He forces words to come out of his mouth – real, proper words, like "Hello, Christine. Funny sort of day, isn't it? Where are you off to?"

In his pocket, the stem of the pipe makes a tiny noise as his tightly clenched hand snaps it.

In his mind, awful and unwanted thoughts invade...

> *She was poor but she was honest*
> *She had legs up to her bum.*

She says, "I'm going to the high street. Goodbans. You know, the drapers. To get some Silko for Mother."

He says, "Oh, Goodbans, good. I mean, yes."

His mind says, *So round, so firm, so fully packed...*

She says, "Like to walk along with me?"

He says, "Well, actually, I'd love to, but you see I can't, it's quarter past and—"

His mind says, *Oh, what a luvverly pair of coconuts.*

She says, "Gosh, is it that late? Another time, then."

He says, "Yes, another time – no look, wait a mo—"

His mind says, *Standing there with her knees all bare, every little wiggle makes the boys all stare.*

Then she's walking away, with her pleated skirt caressing her springy tapered calves and her right breast lifting and bouncing as she turns to wave. Going, going, gone.

His mind says, *Oh, well done, you pathetic little scumbag.*

He takes out his broken briar and dimly stares at it. Five shillings up the spout.

He looks at his watch. Twenty-four minutes past! Oh gawd, oh *gawd.*

He opens, with his own shiny new Yale key, the big, black front door.

He enters his home.

A LITTLE LIE DOWN

He's late! His mother and his sister are already sitting at the round mahogany dining-room table. And they've started eating.

His mother, without looking up, asks, all on one note, "What is the time?"

"Er ... er..." he says, looking at his watch, which shows one twenty-six. "Just after twenty past one."

"Lunch in this house," intones his mother, "is at a quarter past one."

She speaks in the voice of a judge passing sentence on a particularly disgusting criminal. Silently, Nick seats himself, eyes downcast, and picks up knife and fork. Noisily, he fumbles the fork and it clatters and rings on the table. His mother flinches at, but bravely bears, the noise. "After lunch," she announces, "I am going to have a little lie-down. I have one of my headaches."

Nick rams food down his throat. He glances across the table at his sister. She has a round, blonde, delightful face, but there is no delight in it at this moment: it wears the expression so often seen – the guarded, careful, "Really-I'm-perfectly-at-ease" look, the dull cheerfulness of a dutiful daughter. A saintly look. But then, she is a saint compared with her devil of a brother, who, in time with every chew, is silently reciting "Bugger ... bugger ... bugger..."

He steals a glance at his mother, a handsome woman who once must have been a beauty. She has a large body, a sensitive countenance and particularly elegant, slender hands, marred only by a slight orange-brown staining of two fingers. She gets through twenty or more Players full-strength cigarettes a day.

They cost 11$\frac{1}{2}$d. The $\frac{1}{2}$d change buys a D-section finger of Cadbury's milk chocolate. Delicious. Even at his advanced age – sixteen and a half, remember – Nick still relishes the halfpennyworth, his reward for cycling to the shop for another packet of twenty.

The meal ends with tinned tangerines and "coffee cream" – single cream. Tinned tangerines are still a delicacy to him. He almost cheers up. But then the awful weight of his mother's voice descends on him again: "I'll leave you two to do the washing-up" it leadenly pronounces. It might just as well have added, "And you will hang by the neck until you are dead."

Exit mother. Son and daughter enter the scullery, crockery loaded on tray. Now Nick is scowling and gnashing his teeth, furious with himself for being furious. "Why *must* she carry on like that?" he demands. "All that doom and gloom just because I'm a few minutes late!"

"You must remember," his sister says piously, "that she's had a lot to put up with since Father died."

There's no answer to that: it is obviously true. And yet...

"You can wash, if you like," says his sister. "I don't mind drying and putting away."

She really is a saint.

Meanwhile, here's good old Peter at the door. "Want to come up west with me? The Cameo's showing six cartoons – all Disney!"

"OK, hang on, I'll get my cycle clips."

Has Nick enough money for an hour of cartoons? He'll need a shilling (five pence today). Ah, terrific, here's a florin – a ten-pence piece. They're off and away, riding through the slow-moving, easy traffic, through Hammersmith, Earls Court, Kensington, to Piccadilly.

They lean their bikes against the railings around the little cinema. They don't bother to lock them. They buy a tuppenny Mars bar each; and laugh through an hour of Mickey Mouse, Donald Duck and Goofy.

There is a newsreel, too, all about Herr Hitler and his tanks and torchlit, goose-stepping processions (but the tanks are just cardboard, everyone says so);

and about Mussolini, the clownish, big-chinned Italian dictator (but Wops can't fight, everyone says that).

After the show, they tour Soho. Black, brown and yellow faces, faces never seen in suburbia; restaurants with foreign names – Casa Pepe, L'Escargot Bienvenue, Bianchi's; shops displaying drinks he has never heard of, vegetables he has never tasted. And there are cracked-paint doorways leading to forbidden basements, empty all day, thumping with life all night. What goes on down there? Nick visualizes men in sharp suits, bare-shouldered girls, cigarette smoke. Cocktails, jazz.

Jazz! Pete doesn't care about it. But to Nick, jazz is almost an obsession. Some day, soon, he'll go down those shadowed stairways – pass through the doors with shuttered inspection holes – enter dim-lit caverns filled with shuffling dancers, eye-itching smoke and jazz, jazz, jazz.

He'll do it soon, soon. Sooner, in fact, than he thinks.

SOHO CELLAR

Pete says "Ta-ta" and rides off home. Nick stays on.

It is dusk. Already lights are coming on and the chimney-pots of the low Soho buildings are black against the luminous dark blue of the sky. The tarry streets are flushed gold with light from the shops. Shop awnings are pushed up with poles, neon signs flicker and bloom, starlings begin their nightly shrieking aerobatics.

Footsteps click and patter on the pavements, more and more of them, louder and louder. The offices and shops are emptying. Everyone is going home.

No, not everyone. Soon, whole tribes of people will be coming to work. Cypriot waiters, Windmill showgirls (nude!), scene-shifters, gorgeous actresses, wavy-haired leading men – another hour or so and they'll all be there.

Even some jazz-musicians. Look! There's a taxi stopping across the road and the fare is unloading a drum kit! The fare says to the driver, "You might give us a hand."

"Sorry, mate, I'm a driver not a bleeding porter."

"You're a bleeder either way."

Nervously, Nick says, "Shall I help you?"

"Yeah … nice of you … cop hold of this hi-hat."

"And the snare drum?"

"Who told you that's a snare? Educated, aren't you?"

"I like jazz. Mad on it."

"You're mad, all right. Forget it, sonny, jazz is a pain in the arse. Lucky to get a couple of quid a night, and know how much this kit cost me?"

"It's all Selmer stuff so I suppose—"

"More'n a hundred, and some of it's secondhand. Jazz, I don't know, it's a mug's game. Why do I do it? Tell me why!"

"They say the real money's in dance bands—"

"I can't keep off it, that's why. Go easy round this bend … a step at a time … steady…"

"Is Selmer the best make? I've seen pictures of Cozy Cole, he uses Selmer."

"Cozy Cole! Cozy Cole! Another bleeding Yank, bloody genius, he'd sound good on a suitcase. How come you know about Cozy Cole?"

"I listen to Duke Ellington and Fats Waller and Earl Hines and Teddy Bunn—"

"Bloody Teddy Bunn, another bloody black Yank, another bleeding genius. He'd sound good on a ukelele. How do *you* know about *Teddy Bunn*?"

"Records. I play the guitar. I try to be like the guitarists on the records, but—"

"Ever heard of Django Reinhardt?"

"Django! *Django!* He's incredible, amazing!"

"I'll tell you what Django is, he's bloody *impossible*, no one can play like that! Bleeding gypsy Frog, playing like that!"

"I saw him at the Chiswick Empire, it was incredible—"

"I heard him in Paris, France, I was sitting right up against him, bleeding *impossible*!"

HONEYSUCKLE ROSE

The drum kit is set up. It takes a long time adjusting all those butterfly nuts. Now Nick can see the drummer properly, by the single light shining on to the little raised bandstand. The drummer is short, rattish, brilliantined and gap-toothed. His eyes are large, dark and alive with intelligence. He sits at the drums and goes per-DER-shish, per-DER-shish, per-DER-shish on the hi-hat cymbal. His foot drives the drum pedal as if through a metronome. Nick's blood tingles. "That's just terrific," he says. The drummer winks and goes through a series of paradiddles, clean as a machine.

"You say you play guitar?" the drummer asks.

"Yes, well, that is, I—"

"Lennie's guitar's over there, in its case," says the drummer. "Go on, drag it out, have a bash, he won't mind."

"But I—"

"He can't mind if he doesn't know, can he?" says the drummer. "Go on, have a bash. Just put in four in a bar."

"What do I play?"

"*Honeysuckle rose, honeysuckle rose,*" sings the drummer, beating out a soft shuffle. "*You're confectionery, goodness knows, my honeysuckle rose.* Come on, come on, put the chords in. F major. *Every honey bee...*"

Nick hammers out four-in-a-bar on the guitar. The song ends. The drummer makes the cymbal go *ker-CHIZZZ* and says, "You're *all right.*" He seems astonished. "Nice little changes in the middle eight," he says. Nick glows.

"Do you think – do you know any place – where I might sit in?" he asks the drummer.

"No trouble at all. You know the chords, they'll let you— Heh, Pluto! Aren't you at the Jigs?"

Pluto is a black man with a long, doggy face. He holds a trumpet case. The drummer talks to Pluto. Pluto beams, amazing Nick with the number and whiteness of his teeth, and talks to the drummer.

While they talk, Nick is forgotten. He slinks upstairs and out. "Oh, well..." he says. "Oh, well..."

Glumly, he pedals home to the big, safe Victorian house; and Mother.

TWO

GAINFUL EMPLOYMENT

Nick's mother says, "I hope you have been thinking about getting a job."

"Yes, of course, I've been working at it—"

"I can't have you under my feet all day. You are no longer a schoolboy. You must help out. You must have a *job*."

"Yes, of course, I was thinking of—"

"I have arranged for you to see Gareth and Judy. At their flat, next Tuesday, six-thirty. They may be able to help get you a *job*."

"Yes. I see. Next Tuesday. Fine."

A *job*...!

No, wait, please, he protests, things are going too fast! You wanted to be free, didn't you? You wanted to be on your own, liberated from school, independent.

But a *job*! You're too young for a job. What can you do? Nothing. Who wants you? Nobody.

Why can't the world just leave a man alone?

Nevertheless, on Tuesday Nick takes the tube to another London suburb (his mother had to give him the fare) and rings the bell of Gareth and Judy's flat. He takes the modern lift with modern strip lighting and modern buttons to press. It is all very unlike home.

Standing outside the door of No. 11, he hears the clitter-clatter of two typewriters. As usual, Judy and Gareth are hard at work. The sound both excites and frightens Nick. It is exciting because these are real grown-ups, real writers working for money. It is frightening because he wants to be like them. But will he ever be?

He rings the bell. Judy opens the door. "Oh, Nick, of course, is it six-thirty already? Come in, we're both in a mess, I've got to finish a thing for tomorrow and Gareth's got a broadcast, but lovely to see you, come in!"

She is short, plump and not pretty but something better than pretty. She moves quickly, like a bird. Gareth, also short and plump, takes his time about everything, deliberately and amusingly. They set each other off to perfection. Judy works on a portable Corona, Gareth on a portable Underwood. Both machines are surrounded by typing, his neatly stacked and hers in a mess all over the big table. Professionals.

"Your ma, how is she? Says you've got to get a job, she's quite right of course, be a love and put the kettle on, you just flick the switch, oh *bum*, we're out of tea, can you make coffee? Now, about your job—"

Gareth stops prodding at the keys, looks at Nick and says, "A woman called Jean Lang. A theatrical agent. She might give you a job. If she does, take it, my boy. Go down on your benders and take it."

Nick tries to make coffee in their modern electric percolator. He gets it wrong and Judy does it at lightning speed, splash, tinkle, jingle, clatter.

Gareth has prepared a letter of introduction for Nick to hand to Jean Lang. It is very short and completely convincing, a masterpiece. Lucky Jean Lang, you'd think, getting such a brilliant young man to work for her!

Nick wants to stay and enjoy the energy fizzing around Gareth and Judy. But he knows he must leave because he is an intruder, six feet of gangling young wet blanket. He goes.

He has one and eight pence in his pockets. He does not want to go home, so he takes a bus ride that ends up in Soho.

Wardour Street, Frith Street, bookshops, music shops, restaurants, yellow electric lights, grimy old buildings. It feels like home yet he knows himself to be a stranger. But there is the doorway leading down to the club where he met the drummer. And there's music. Might as well try...

MEMBERS ONLY

Once again, Nick goes down the narrow stairway and turns the sharp corner at the bottom where the bass drum nearly got stuck. This time, however, something has changed: he is cut off from the bump-bump-bump and blare of the music by a blank, grey, solid door with a square porthole at eye-level. He doesn't know what to do. He ponders.

At last he knocks on the door. No reply. He knocks again. A slide behind the porthole whips aside and an amazing eye fills the space. The eye is black surrounded by veined yellow, surrounded in turn with glistening black flesh. It is a really nasty eye.

"What you want?" says the eye. It keeps blinking. Why? Because of the stale smoke leaking out around it. Cigarette smoke from inside the club.

"Who are you?" says the eye. Nick mumbles his name.

"No one that name here," says the eye. The porthole slams shut.

A miracle happens: footsteps coming down the stairs – voices – and there he is! The drummer! Chance in a million.

"Wouldn't let you in, eh!" he says. "Guitar, wasn't it? Nice little chords." He gives the door a kick. The eye reappears.

"Come on then," the drummer says, "open up them pearly gates."

"Who that with you?"

"Friend of mine. Guitarist. He's all right."

"No member, only members."

"Bugger that. I'll sign him in. Open up."

And they're in.

It is a long, low basement, filled with a surging ocean of swaying figures, dimly seen. Beyond them is the brighter focal point: the band. A black face behind a golden trumpet; a slithering silvery trombone powered by a coffee-coloured head and hands; a mop of hair, all that's visible of a bass player: a hunched, tousled boy pianist hardly older than Nick; a swarthy, villainous guitarist with a hooked nose; and a squat, thickset drummer, black, with puffy, drugged, half-closed eyes.

The din is amazing and delightful.

"Dreamer!" Nick's friend the drummer shouts in Nick's ear.

"What?"

"That drummer. We call him the Dreamer. Always looks dozy."

"He's great!" The drums go *a-chizz, chizz, a-rick-ety-tick, a-boom-chic-a-BOOM*.

"He's bloody useless. Accelerates. Can't you hear? Always accelerating. Can't hold a tempo."

"Those eyes ... he looks as if he's on drugs." Nick knows nothing about drugs, but still...

"That's not drugs, that's cos he's bloody dim. Useless. Keeps accelerating."

"Will you be playing?"

"About nine, maybe ten. Have a beer."

The bar is small but as big as the bandstand. "Who he?" says the woman behind the bar. She is a large, beige-skinned lady with a huge cleavage and big, dark suspicious eyes.

"Friend of mine, wossisname," says the drummer. "Great guitarist." Aside, he says, "What's your name?"

"Nick."

"I'm Freddie, right? Freddie."

To the woman, he says, "Nick, meet Mrs Jack. Mrs Jack meet Nick."

"You a member?" says Mrs Jack, glaring at Nick. "You not a member, you get out of here." She glares sideways, spits into a small glass, polishes it on her skirt and pours gin into it. She lifts the glass to her great red mouth, brings it down empty. "You musicians," she says. "All lying pigs. Little pig men!" And suddenly she blazes into peals of laughter that jig her earrings and bounce her creamy bosom. She pours two glasses of beer and turns away to answer the telephone. "No, no," she shouts above the noise of the band. "Not unless he's a member. Ten shillings."

"Mrs Jack," Freddie says, shaking his head. "She's all right, you know? Bloody barmy but all right. Killed Jack, her old man, knifed him, straight up. Cheers."

Once the place must have seated people. There is still a line of linked, tattered cinema seats against one wall. Nick sits down, glad to be out of sight but able to see.

Couples dance. Black and coffee-coloured men; too-white white girls in shiny dresses, black stockings, greasy scarlet lipstick, bleachy hair. They dance badly. The men move as easily as cats; when they are not dancing two might face each other and talk, both at once, not listening, just smiling and talking, with the palms of their hands lazily facing forward. Everything they do looks easy, meaningless but amiable.

There's a half-size billiard table. The cover has a tear in it. Three men play, talking all the time, not minding when someone's backside gets in the cue's way. One man wears a fawn curly-brimmed Derby hat and smokes a cigar in a holder. He is like a character actor in a Hollywood movie. He even has two gold teeth. "That's Chappie da Silva," the drummer says. "Plays trumpet. Owns the Nic Nac Club."

"Is he good on trumpet?" Nick asks.

"Bloody useless. Secondhand Louis Armstrong."

"And the guitarist?"

"Oh, him. He'd be all right if you could hear him. Back in the States," he says, his voice turning American, "they got amps, you know? Amplifiers. Real snazzy, man, know what I mean?"

At about nine-thirty, Freddie is on drums. He is fast, neat and a showman. He takes a solo – becomes, for thirty-two bars, the star. He spins a stick up and catches it. He winks at the girls. He throws his head back, closes his eyes, does the showbiz. He's good. The other musicians take no notice; the trumpeter shakes spit out of his trumpet, the guitarist lights a cigarette, the bass player chats to the trombonist.

Nick realizes that it must take a lot to become accepted by jazz musicians as a jazz musician.

An hour later, a fight starts. Two slim, dark-suited young Jamaicans scream falsetto obscenities. They face each other crouching low, eye-whites showing, beautiful teeth whiter than white, long-fingered left hands clawing in front of them.

Then something glints and a girl screams "A-owww!" and blood squirts on to the dingy paint-work of the wall and Mrs Jack sails in with a parrot screech and a flailing dishcloth.

What was it that glinted? Good God! An open razor, a cut-throat! Mrs Jack has taken it away from the unwounded man. "Pig!" she shouts at him. "You a member, heh? OK, not no more a member, you a pig and get out!"

The band goes in to *Moten Swing*, C major.

The cut man has the bloodied dishcloth knotted round his forearm. Shaking like a leaf, eyes jittering, mouth twitching, he dances with his girl.

GODS AND GODDESSES

Nick is on his way to his new job. He got it straight away. Jean Lang turned out to be an instantly delightful, larger-than-life person with a loud clear voice, a plump, moon-like face with mischievous corners to the mouth and a straight-to-the-point way of dealing with anything at all.

"You can type?" she says. "Really? Show me." He shows her, on a big, upright black Underwood. "That'll do. You *can* type. Boys can't, they're not taught, I can't think why."

The phone rings. "Let's see you answer it," she says. Her amused brown eyes regard him, judging his performance. "Hello? Yes ... yes ... hang on, I'll see if she is available." He puts his hand over the receiver and says, "Someone called Polly Marklin. Are you here?"

"No, definitely not. But be nice."

"I'm so sorry... You'll ring again? Yes, please do, thank you."

He put down the phone.

"Brilliant!" she says. "You did that just right. You and me, we'll get on like a house on fire. Never, never admit that I'm in – that's rule number one. Always, always make a note of who called; make a list and give it to me every half hour. I'll give *you* a list of my specials, the people you must put straight through. Understood?"

"Yes."

"Good. Now your hair. It looks ridiculous. Here's ten shillings. I'll phone – no, *you* phone – Michael's in Charing Cross Road and get it cut. Ask for Mr Paul. Seven shillings plus one shilling tip, that makes eight. Keep the change to buy lunch, then come back and get started. Lovely. Oh, money: you'll get two pounds a week, it's no good arguing, they're the world's meanest here. And don't try to fiddle the petty cash, Miss Hardcastle knows all the dodges. Oh, the phone, blast..."

Nick loves her: her confidence, her directness, her energy – and her power: for she is London's top play agent, a force in the major literary/theatrical agency.

He sees the power that first afternoon, when the most beautiful woman in the world enters like a scented whirlwind. "Where's Jean, quick, darling – I'm frantic, furious – where *is* she?"

He tries to hold her back. It should be easy. The lady is tiny – five-foot-three? Size two lizard-skin shoes? She wears a little black hat with velvet dots spotting a black half-veil. But her eyes are enormous – brilliant green, apparently lit up from inside, rimmed with mascara outside.

She is a household name, a great talent, a notable beauty, a star, a goddess.

"I'm sorry, but—" says Nick.

"Oh, bugger, bugger, *bugger*!" cries the goddess, flailing at Nick with little gloved hands. She picks up a telephone directory and throws it. It misses the frosted-glass panels separating him from his boss and merely knocks down Jean Lang's latest pot plant. "You stupid urchin!" screeches the goddess. "I WANT JEAN!"

Jean's half-glass door is flung open and Jean is there, plump chin lifted. "Any more of that," she tells the goddess, "and you won't get a free cup of tea."

"Oh, Jean...! Jean darling...! Everyone's being so awful, and Larry won't lift a *finger*..." The goddess is crying, quite beautifully, into a lacy handkerchief, without disturbing her mascara.

"First, darling," Jean commands, "we will mind our manners and say hello *nicely* to my Mr Nicholas here. One day he may let you call him Nick."

"Oh, darling Jean, darling Nick ... oh, isn't he lovely, I *know* we're going to be such friends, how do you do!" He holds for half a second a tapered, weightless hand.

Then – "Oh, Jean, everyone's being such a bitch! What *am* I to do?"

"Nick, ring for tea. Come on, love, tell Mother all about it."

The door closes for half an hour. The phone rings incessantly. A drunken Irish playwright, world-famous, comes in to borrow half a crown. An actor, world-famous, makes an agonized entrance in a camel-hair coat – "Oh *God*, I've *got* to see Jean". A dimpling, elderly comedienne-turned-successful-playwright flirts with Nick to get him to hold her nasty little dog.

Nick loves all of it.

BRITAIN'S DJANGO

Nick begins to settle in. He finds bed-and-board away from home. This costs thirty shillings a week and leaves him ten shillings for tube fares to work and lunches in dingy restaurants. There is nothing left over for toothpaste, a night out or Stick-a-Soles for his shoes.

However, he has his Blue Bird portable typewriter and can steal paper and carbons. Even as a boy at boarding school, the typewriter sometimes earned him a pound or two. He'd write "Party Games for the Kiddies", anything at all, send off the typescript to magazines and newspapers, and hope. The editors who received the stuff were not to know that the writer was a schoolboy. All they saw was a neat typescript. Sometimes they liked what they saw.

He also has his guitar, a cheap Coletti that looks better than it sounds. It has no volume, it doesn't make enough noise. Feeling like a criminal, he wheedles twenty-two pounds out of Gareth and Judy and buys, in the Charing Cross Road – then as now full of music shops – a big, loud-voiced Clifford Essex.

"Hang around in Archer Street, by the Windmill Theatre," says Freddie. "We all go there. Tea in the caff, then out on the street again till some fixer comes by." Nick hangs around and a fixer does come by, muttering "Guitar player, guitar player". Nick, pig ignorant, puts in the chords at bus depots, town hall dances, stuffy local dances, weird all-night clubs.

He is pig ignorant in several ways. In a jazz club in St John's Wood, of all places, a little drunken man with a filthy collar and crooked tie keeps putting his ear against the guitar and saying "Britain's Django Reinhardt! Fantastic!" He insists that Nick has one of his cigarettes. Nick is a pipe-smoker, but he gives in. The cigarette is skinny and pale yellow. It tastes of burning straw.

"Oh, fantastic, Britain's Django Reinhardt!" says the little drunk. "Have another ciggie, be my guest! Go on, it's the real jive!"

"Well, if you insist," says Nick, and he smokes away, not enjoying it.

Only much later does he discover that "the real jive" can mean "real marijuana" – that the cigarettes were reefers, grass, mezz, drugs. He learns this when the little man's photograph appears in the news-paper: DRUG BARON'S HEAVY JAIL SENTENCE.

But the cigarettes have no effect on Nick what-soever. What *does* affect him is gin.

In many of the clubs where jazz is played, the musicians get little in the way of money: their reward is an endless supply of small gins, placed on the special chair next to the player's chair. Soon, he is so steeped in gin that when he takes a bath, the water smells of it. He knows that gin is Mother's Ruin – that he will be a shuffling moron if he keeps on like this. But clubs are hot, smoky places, your mouth gets dry. Ah, here's a gin... But gin dries the mouth too. So he soon needs another gin.

How does all this low-life and high living affect his health? Does he totter, after his night hours in the clubs, bleary-eyed to work next morning?

Not often. He is too heavily occupied, too sleep-less. And still young.

Young. He really is very young. Look at him again.

He is now seventeen or eighteen, six feet tall, pink-faced, still wearing flappy grey trousers, a ginger tweed sports coat and a nice tie. Admittedly his hair doesn't look as stupid as it did – Mr Paul went "Tck! tck! oh dearie me, like a spider's lounge!" – and he smokes his pipe without choking.

But he must seem a bit of a freak among those notabilities of stage and screen at the play agent's; and among those dangerous black, brown and over-painted faces in the clubs.

Nick's pig ignorance is his saving grace. There is so much he doesn't know: yet his ignorance seldom matters.

Music, for instance. He earns as much or more money playing as he earns in his respectable job: but he cannot read music. Not a note.

He cannot even understand what is shouted to him, in mid-tinkle, by pianists. "G major, C7th, then into B flat and E flat for the middle eight, OK?" they tell him over their shoulders. Nick nods, looks wise, and keeps thumping out four in a bar.

Amazingly, he almost always gets it right. He has a terrific ear for chords, changes, modulations.

"I like a thirteenth in the release," says a pianist. Nick is cunning enough to say, "Come again? Didn't hear you."

"A thirteenth. Like this." Mercifully, this time the pianist *plays* the notes.

"Oh, yes, a thirteenth." Once he has heard it, Nick can play it straight back on his guitar.

It is both a gift and a passport.

OPPOSITE SEX

Nick's pig ignorance embraces girls. Or rather, fails to embrace them. He cannot believe that any girl he admires could possibly admire him. And when, by chance, he finds himself in the right place at the right time with the right girl, he is baffled by her behaviour.

Rita, over there, standing alone by the bar of the Jive Club... Just look at her! The red of her lips, the flash of her eyes, the roll of her hips, the curve of her thighs (Nick often finds himself thinking in bad verse) — it isn't fair to make them like that, sugar and spice and all things nice, oh, you beautiful doll, you small, sweet beautiful doll, let me put my arms around you...

Some hope. She goes with Rex, a jazz journalist, an ancient man of thirty-something, a man who buys her things and takes her about in his Railton car. It isn't fair, it isn't fair.

Rita is bored out of her mind. She drinks a gin-and-something that Rex will pay for later. But Rex is late, Rita needs amusement. She flashes her eyes at Nick! And again! And she's smiling at him, a slight and secret smile, surely she can't mean...?

He goes across to her, smiles shakily and says, "I say ... hello ... not many people here yet." A brilliant opening gambit.

Yet she replies! She even smiles! "You haven't got a drink," she says. "You're Nick, aren't you? Guitarist, right? Mmmm... I love guitar players." Wisps of steam curl upwards from Nick's ears.

Rita has a new flat. It is near Notting Hill Gate. "Oh, but I'd love you to see it," she says. "And bring your guitar, if you feel like playing. Do you like to play? I do."

Then Rex is pushing through the crowd round the bar, grinning, slapping backs, catching the barman's eye, being Well Known and Popular. "Cripes, kid," he says to Rita, "bloody BBC, they'll drive me mad, won't make up their minds. Who's this?"

"Nick," says Rita. "Nick Thing. Bloody BBC, poor you."

Now their backs are turned to Nick. Rex's back is glaring windowpane check with padded shoulders. Hers is creamy, warm, silken flesh.

"Let's scram," Rita says to Rex. "Take me somewhere *interesting*."

They go without a backward glance.

It isn't fair.

Or take Christine Endersleigh, the girl Nick hoped and dreaded to meet on the pavement outside his home.

He meets her once more, again by accident, at almost the same spot.

Somehow she seems different. Her legs, body and head form the same luscious assembly: they should cause Nick's ears to fizz. Somehow, they don't. Could it be the single row of small pearls or the angora jumper or the brogue shoes that put him off?

"Christine! It must be almost two years! What are you up to these days?"

She has a job with a wholesale firm, actually. In the City, as a matter of fact. Actually, it's a marvellous position, such a nice crowd to work with. One big, happy family, as they say.

"I've never played Happy Families," he says. "But I'd love to try it with you."

She laughs uncertainly and briefly. He laughs dashingly and too long. "Where are you off to now?" he says.

"Oh, just popping in for a cup of tea, actually. Here, at home. You can come if you like."

"No, I'd be in the way. Your people."

"Actually, everyone's out. I'm on my ownsome."

"In that case..."

Once indoors, things warm up rapidly.

"I'll just get changed while the kettle boils," she says. She dashes out, silken legs flashing, and returns transformed. Now she wears shoes with heels, a pleated skirt that swings, and a tight, silky blouse with lots of small glass buttons that don't look up to their job.

"Hang on a sec," she says. "The kettle's boiling. Tea in a jiff. Do you take sugar?"

"I don't care either way," he answers truthfully. For he is sitting on a big, wide, soft sofa. Presumably she will sit beside him.

She does. She pours tea, tops up the pot. Each little movement sets off sympathetic jigglings of her various parts: harmonic vibrations. The tea cools. Nick warms.

"Tell me all your news," he says.

"Well, the really *big* news, actually," she replies, "is that I'm about to be engaged."

All at once, a chill descends. Even the little glass blouse buttons seem to lose their glitter.

"Oh, gosh, super, great," says Nick. "Anyone I know?"

"Well, I don't know if you actually know him. Trevor Rice."

"*Trevor Rice?*"

"We're waiting to announce it after he's got through his Intermediates. Chartered accountancy."

"Not *Trevor Rice!*" he says, appalled. "Not Old Wobblebum!"

He had not intended to say the last words. Fortunately she does not hear them. "He'll end up fully qualified in due course," she says. She goes on and on about chartered accountancy.

He does not listen. Trevor Rice! Old Wobblebum! Nick remembers him all right. Trevor got his nickname because of his unusual shape. Trevor is – Nick discovered the word – steatopygous: that is, he suffers from an excessive development of fat on the buttocks. He then tapers off, above and below, like a pair of brackets (). His little fat feet point inwards. His small head, with surprised-looking boiled eyes, emerges straight from his body without the benefit of a neck. At school, he was a swot – first in every boring subject. His parents have two cars, one of them a Daimler. They throw their rose garden open to the public every summer.

"*Trevor Rice!*" says Nick for the third time. "But Christine! You bloody can't!"

And now, once again, his pig ignorance is revealed to him. For Christine, without changing expression or raising her voice, looks straight at him and says, "Oh yes, I bloody *can*, actually. And I will."

"But marry Trevor! Why?"

"For the money," she says, pouring more tea. "And to get away from Mummy, and living at home, and not having nice things. More tea?"

He is stunned. He had genuinely thought that lovely girls were filled with lovely thoughts. Sugar and spice and all things nice.

"And then there're clothes," Christine says, giving him, with a steady hand, his cup of tea. "I do like nice clothes. I mean, I *need* them. It's the way I am. I mean, I might want to be an actress."

"But you've got nice clothes," Nick mumbles. "You look smashing. I mean, look at you now!"

"Oh, you like this?" Christine says. "This blouse? I suppose it is quite nice, actually." She begins to finger the tiny glass buttons. "They sometimes come undone," she says calmly.

Again, she looks him straight in the eye. "Mummy will be back in less than an hour," she says. She moves closer to him.

Mummy has still not returned. Christine washes up the tea cups, plumps up the sofa cushions and says, "Trevor never does things like *that*." She gives Nick the sort of approving smile a nursing Sister might give a patient who reports a good bowel movement.

She begins to hum a song that he particularly hates – *The Chapel in the Moonlight*. It makes him itch.

"Was it nice?" he says.

"Mmmm! mmmm!" she replies wrinkling her nose fetchingly. "*When we're strolling down the aisle*," she sings, "*Where roses entwine*." Then – "I think you'd better go, actually. Mummy could be back at any moment."

"Shall I see you again?"

"Oh, I shouldn't think so, actually. I mean, I'm almost engaged."

"That's right, so you are. To Trevor. Well, I'll be off."

He never sees her again.

THE SAD SACK

Nick is on his way, five or ten minutes late as usual (Jean Lang is never late), to his job in Covent Garden.

He hurries along the pavement, feeling muddy wetness seeping through the shoe sole with the hole in it.

He sees, crouching in the gutter, the black cats, a special skinny breed with a furless patch from eye to ear. They chew fiercely at sprouts. Vegetarians.

He sees the porters' barrows with the names of wholesalers or hirers deeply engraved in the chassis woodwork; the engravers use a florid, sloping script.

He sees and hears the porters, half running over the damp, shining cobbles, balancing towers of wicker baskets that sway above their cloth caps.

He loves what he sees. He cannot imagine it ever changing.

"Quick, quick, late again, don't apologize, bash out this contract," Jean says. She thrusts papers into his hands. "Do you speak French? O Lord above, neither do I. I'm on *this* phone. When *that* phone rings, say '*Monsieur Edward arrive bientôt*', got that? Well, let me hear you say it. Oh well, that will have to do I suppose..."

To her phone, she says, "No, darling, he lives in Albany. Not *the* Albany, you're not supposed to say 'the'. No love, I don't know why and does it matter very much? Well, get down there, take a taxi, I'll phone in advance to say you're coming. And *don't talk terms*. Anything you like, but *don't talk terms*."

She turns to Nick and says, "From now on, we're making our own coffee in this Cona thing. I can't stand the firm's coffee anymore so you're in charge of it. Read the instructions, I can't make head or tail of them, catch hold. Oh, and I've got you another job, but we'll talk about that later. There's your phone. *Monsieur Edward arrive bientôt*, remember? Then just fake it. Make nice noises."

As the phone rings, Monsieur Edward himself arrives. He wears a tweed cape, a silk kerchief, a long cigar and hand-made shoes. He writes farces and has been a success for thirty years. "Darling Jean, *dear* Nicholas, is that Louis? There, you see, timing, perfect timing, here I am and there he is... *Ah, Louis, mon vieux, comment ça va?*"

He rattles away in machine-gun French. He hands his bothersome cigar to Nick to take care of ("Dear boy ... *would you?*"). He makes notes on his Morocco-leather notepad with a gold-banded Waterman pen. He mentions sums of thousands of pounds and millions of francs.

Nick feels sick with envy and despair.

It isn't fair, it isn't fair.

"You said you've got me another job?" he reminds Jean Lang.

"Oh yes, marvellous news, just what you want—"

"But I don't want another job, I like being here with you."

"Nonsense, you're wasted here. And then there's

the money, you'll get nowhere here. I've got you more money, there, cheer up, *more money*! Give your auntie Jean a lovely smile and say 'Goody-goody'."

"I want to stay here."

"You start, let me see, the first of next month just round the corner with Caslon Gill's. Of course you know about them, don't you? You don't? They publish all the plays. Everything from Ibsen to Billy Bennet monologues. You'll be doing the amateur rights and you'll get fifteen shillings a week more, *fifteen shillings*!"

"You're giving me the sack, aren't you?"

"Oh, dear Nick love, of course not, we've got on like a house on fire, you've been a treasure. And such wonderful coffee. But it's shorthand, you see, you haven't got it and I really do need someone with shorthand. Dear Nick, don't look like that."

He wants to cry but is far too old.

THREE

WING COLLARS AND JACKBOOTS

Nick has become so old that he thinks, quite often, about World War II.

When he was a schoolboy, he saw newspaper photographs of the great parades held by the Fascist dictators, Hit and Muss, and knew the jokes about cardboard tanks. Not funny. Surely cardboard tanks would be just as difficult to make as real ones? Surely men as grotesquely lunatic as Hit and Muss – and whole nations mad enough to make gods of them – had to be taken seriously? Mad dogs are taken seriously...

And now bombs are falling, regularly, on London. Sometimes they narrowly miss Nick. The war is real.

Nick remembers the declaration of war. He had been standing outside his aunt's house in Sussex, by the sea, overhearing the news on his cousin's big radiogram. He smelled the climbing roses – it was September – and felt the sun's warmth – it was a nice day. He heard the enfeebled, creaking voice of Britain's leader, Prime Minister Neville Chamberlain. Even the boomy speakers couldn't give that voice virility.

Poland had been invaded by Nazi Germany; Britain had asked Hitler to withdraw his troops. "No such assurance having been received," said the weary voice, "I have to tell you that we are now in a state of war with Germany." The voice went on to say that all this was a frightful blow to him personally, he had always hoped, but dear, oh dear, and there we are.

To Nick, all this seemed inevitable. The preliminary rounds had gone on for years. Our man went into the ring armed with an umbrella, a wing collar and horselike teeth: their men bellowed in wearing tricky military uniforms, jackboots and every weapon from Luger pistols to tanks and bombers. Our man's supporters were negotiators, politicians, appeasers, grey old men; their men's supporters were armed, uniformed, fanatical young thugs, trained and equipped for the main event.

As the Prime Minister finished his speech, the air-raid sirens went off. Nick thought he should fall flat on the ground or put a saucepan over his head – do something dramatic. But what?

It was just as well that he did nothing. Almost immediately, the sirens sounded the All Clear. Then followed the Phoney War, the Bore War, the period when things failed to happen. It lasted for months.

Nick had forgotten the war and concentrated on more vital matters concerning himself.

MAYBE A BUTLER

Then the Phoney War is over, the real war is on and the Blitz – the night-bombing of London – is raging.

Most people shelter in their own homes. There are

indoor, table-top Morrison shelters like big rabbit hutches; and outdoor Anderson shelters made of corrugated-iron sections. Dig a big hole, bolt the sections together, cover the whole thing with garden soil. But we have the cellar.

The rich people sit out the war in luxury hotels whose basements become their home-from-home. "Oh, Mr Finching-Llowndes, I've been such a goose, I've spilt my Ovaltine all over my quilt!" "Tut-tut, dear lady, permit me to assist."

For the poor and unprotected, there are free-standing public shelters in the streets. Bleak brick blocks. They are horrible places. They smell of urine and unwashed clothes and bodies. You cannot read in them, there is too little light. You can't sit comfortably, the wooden seats are like wall-mounted planks. They have a daytime reputation as focal points for molesters, rapists and murderers. At night, during the raids, they are plain and simply horrible. And dangerous. Something was wrong with the design. Heavy roofs fall in. Bomb blast may sneak round the curtain-wall entrance.

Nick avoids public shelters. But sometimes he nips inside one when the bombers are right overhead.

He stands (the regulars all have their seats), pipe in mouth ("'Ere, put that out, mate, you know the rules."), his face scowling impatiently, his guitar case held upright so that people won't trip over it (they might damage his guitar and then what would he do?) and his face twitching with impatience.

Everyone else is patient. There are Thermos flasks, knitting, draughts, sing-songs and whining kids. ("Mum, I've got to *go*, I can't hold back no longer! Mum, Mum, *Mummmmm!*")

The bombers move on, Nick makes his escape. He travels by Underground. The tube stations themselves become bomb shelters. The Authorities tried to stop it: but the people bought tuppenny tickets, entered the stations and then forgot to travel.

The Authorities gave in. White lines were drawn along the platforms. *Bedding must not extend beyond the lines until 7.30. After the rush hour, you are permitted to move forward another four feet.*

Families and groups of neighbours take over the platforms, staking out their claim to their regular places by sending young Maureen down in the afternoon. The rest of the family arrives in the evening complete with bedding, board games, suitcases, pillows, blankets and potties. They make themselves comfortable for the night. There is light, warmth and the snug feeling that the bombs can't reach you. (But they can: there are ugly rumours, later found to be true, of a direct hit on such-and-such a station ... straight down the lift shaft ... then the water from the burst mains to finish 'em off, poor bleeders.)

Smells, lice, feet treading on your face, sudden screeches and shouts as quarrels break out, a child being sick; those nights in the tube must be long nights, Nick thinks as he hurries past the tangled knots of bodies under the cheery posters on the tiled walls.

"Your Courage, Your Determination, Your Something-or-Other, Will See Us Through!" Bloody cheek, Nick thinks: who are the *Us* who are going

to be seen through? Politicians in Anthony Eden hats and winged collars?

"Cheers! Cheers! I've got my wings! Now we can look at some Bravington rings!" A cartoon of a jolly fighter pilot about to get engaged to a glamorous blonde.

"Uniform Opinion... Leave It to Austin Reed." More glamorous people, an officer and his bit of crumpet. They look nothing like this worms' nest of *real* people, the troglodytes in cheap shoes, sweaty clothes...

There's an old man taking out his dentures. He's got a little beaker to put them in. There's a toddler peeing against the wall.

Pity he didn't pee on the live rail, that would learn him. Oh, come on, cut it out, nark it, Nick tells himself, what do you expect people to do? How do you expect them to be? All clean-limbed and splendid and unafraid? Are the men all to be Errol Flynn, the movie star? Are all the women to be Greer Garson, who emerges from a Hollywood version of the Blitz with one curl slightly disarranged and one smudge on her Max-Factored left cheek? These bodies sprawled all over the platform are the real thing, the stuff of history.

All the same, he's glad when the tube train's doors slide shut and cut him off from them.

Nick leaves the tube at Sloane Square and hurries eastward, lugging his guitar in its case. The sirens sounded at about the usual time, an hour ago. Now it is pitch black, no street lamps, no lighted windows (*"Put that light out!"*), no glaring car headlamps (the lenses are covered with tin discs with a slotted cocoa-tin thing at the centre). In any case, there are hardly any private cars about.

He is on his way to the "Number One". Once it had been the genteel West End home of someone fairly rich: now it is partly Civil Defence post, partly offices and partly jazz club. He was supposed to be there at eight-thirty. It is already eight-forty.

"Go away!" he mutters to the sky as he shambles on. "Scarper!" He is talking to the Nazi bombers. They are up there, all right. Somewhere south of the river searchlight beams are blossoming and prodding, ack-ack guns are thumping. And, oh gawd, now he can hear the bombers' engines, a low, sullen, pulsing, in-and-out-of-phase rumble, coming closer and closer. "Please!" he begs the sky, "please lay off!"

He has good reason to be frightened. He was half an hour late for the gig last night. He had to unpack his guitar and fumble his way out on to the little stage in the middle of "Tea for Two". People in the audience tittered and André, the lead sax player, had given him a dirty look. And now this bloody air-raid.

What he dreads happens. There's a series of whoompf ... *Whoompf* ... WHOOOMPF! explosions, they're dropping sticks of bombs nearer, suppose an air-raid warden—

"'Ere, *you*!" a voice shouts. "Take bleedin' cover, you bleedin' lunatic, get yerself over *'ere*, come on now, look sharp!"

An air-raid warden, of course. Oh well, better obey. He shelters under a sandbagged archway with the warden. Every time a bomb drops, the warden makes a comment. "Bleedin' shrapnel," he says, as something whizzes down from the sky and smashes the slates of a nearby roof. "More trouble than bleedin' bombs."

Or, "What's in that case, then? Bleedin' banjo? You a Nigger Minstrel?"

Or, as a bomb falls so close that you can hear the tinkle of falling glass, "Cor, chase me Aunt Fanny round the gasworks."

Nick sneers silently at this. He knows where the warden got it from – Nathaniel Gubbins' column in the *Sunday Express*. A real war hero, Nat Gubbins: a truth teller. Bet he never gets a medal when it's all over (and he doesn't).

A bomb smashes a building a hundred yards across the road. The building shrugs its shoulders, lifts its chimney as if raising its hat, belches coloured flames, then slowly slides into a heap of rubble. Soon it is hidden by its own dust. The warden mutters something about a five-hundred-pounder, grabs Nick's arm and says, "Come *on*, then."

Nick comes on. He tears at the rubble with his hands until bells ring and fire engines and CD trucks arrive. Then he is given a pick. He is glad of the pick: you can't play guitar with bruised, cut fingers.

"One over here," says a fireman. "Easy now... You all right, mate? All right, are you?"

It is an elderly man, very thin, wearing a sort of striped waistcoat. The ghastly face is masked in plaster dust. A butler? "There you are, mate, coming along nicely, soon have you out, you're all right."

But the man is not all right. There is only the upper half of him left... Shiny wet tubing...

Then back to digging. The bombers are gone. The wrecked building sags, creaks, grumbles and sometimes suffers minor collapses. Otherwise, it is almost silent and Nick sometimes hears the thump-thump-thump of a bass drum and a trumpet playing. *Jeepers creepers, where d'you get those peepers?*

So he won't reach the club till the second session. And he'll get another dirty look from André.

THE SLIDE

In that same club, Nick's pig ignorance of the opposite sex is demonstrated to him yet again.

Sometimes – not often enough – a starlet descends and twinkles in the warm dimness of the club room. She is a classic English rose, golden-haired, blue-eyed, fragrant, dainty, winsome.

"Oh, darling Fats Waller!" she cries, clasping her red-nailed hands over her whipped-cream bosom. "Oh, do play something by Fatsie!"

She radiates girl-glow and star-appeal (soon, she will indeed be a Hollywood Star). The glow irradiates Nick's pink cheeks and also the leathery, dark cheeks of the drummer, Tiny. "I gonna getchew, Sweet-ness," he mutters. "Getchew laid flat." Nick sees a mental picture of the English Rose with a writhing worm – Tiny – in its bud. First he is sickened, then he laughs. It could never happen, of course.

They play. She claps. They drink gins. She drinks something expensive. The music gets hotter. She shouts, "Whoopee!" and knocks over a table.

The impossible happens. She is sprawling on a sofa, giggling, and Tiny is all over her, mouthing affectionate obscenities and fondling her left leg.

But rescue is at hand. With a bound, Nick is at her side. "I say!" he says, "look here! You can't—"

An invisible something comes up from the couch and hits his face. His last conscious thought is, That's interesting, you really *do* see stars.

He comes to flat on his back looking up at the vision of loveliness kneeling over him. The starlet's hand is stroking his forehead, her lips and eyes are wide with concern. Nick is delighted. This is as it should be.

But the pretty picture changes. The starlet begins to giggle, then to laugh out loud. He rubs his jaw and mutters, "What's so funny?"

"I'm awfully sorry," she says, "but when he hit you, you slid."

Later, Nick learns that drumming is only a hobby for Tiny. His proper job is professional boxing.

He also learns that the starlet's hobby is small, dark boxers with bunchy muscles and plenty of staying power.

Tiny is an up-and-comer, so is she. They are a perfect couple.

BLITZ

The war, in the shape of the Blitz, comes closer and closer to the family home. Eventually it comes so close that it makes Nick's ears ring.

Meanwhile, he has quit his bed-and-breakfast lodgings to live at home. The family must stick together because it might be blown apart.

The big cellar is now the family's air-raid shelter and dormitory. Uncle Rob, a maker of stained glass

windows and other beautiful things for churches,
is a long-time family friend: he has installed great
wooden props to make one part of the cellar a
safety cell. Often, Uncle Rob comes over – he lives
not far away – to see the family through the Blitz
nights.

What nights they are! Candles, paraffin lamps,
torches, buckets, Primus stove to make tea, cushions, quilts, blankets, deckchairs, board games,
paperbacks, sandwiches ... and Nick, his sister, his
mother and Uncle Rob, together in the candlelit
gloom, breathing in coal dust and the cosy fumes of
the Valor oil stove.

That is the picture down there. Outside is the
clamped-down dark of the blackout – always un-
familiar and surprising; the inevitable wail of the
sirens announcing the punctual arrival of the
bombers; and the occasional tin-hatted warden, looking for punishable chinks of light escaping the blackout curtains. But the warden is outside, Nick and his
family are in the cellar.

"Look, don't cheat! You threw a four, not a six!"

"It was a six, you know it was. You're a rotten
loser, that's your trouble."

"Nark it, it was a four! Play fair, throw again."

"Not on your nelly. I'm taking six. One, two,
three, four..."

But then Mother says, "Quiet for a moment...!
Listen."

Everyone lifts their head to listen. Uncle Rob
grunts and refills his pipe, carefully. *Ooooom ... oom
... ooooom* – the bombers. *Booomp! Boomp – oomp!*
The thud of the ack-ack guns. But very far away.

"I'll make tea," says Sister.

"No, my turn, I'll do it," says Nick, noble and unselfish for once in his life. Who knows, this might be the very last time any of them drink tea. When he gets to heaven and St Peter asks "What was your last act on Earth?" he will be able to say, "I made tea for everyone." And he'll get in.

No, wait: Nick does not believe any of this. Bombs will fall, but none will touch him. Houses will be knocked flat, bodies dragged out, the family cat discovered covered in dust and stiff as a board – but all that is for someone else, not him.

Up in the sky, there are young men called Hans or Helmut or Heinrich. The ack-ack is spattering their Heinkels with hot metal, shattering Perspex, throwing their aircraft about in great rending jerks. But they are Nazis, alien beings. His imagination can encompass the existence of them and their Heinkels, Dorniers and Messerschmitts, but he is him and they are something else. Never the twain shall meet. Nothing to fear.

It is different for his mother. Even his ingrown imagination has come to realize this. For her, every crump-*crump*-CRUMP shakes her older, tenderer frame. Worse, it stirs fears for her children.

"Oh, Ma, don't make such a fuss, that lot was miles away!" he might have said, when he first saw her eyes widen with fear and her lips tremble. He wouldn't say it now. He understands that she is frightened all right, certainly: but mainly for him and his sister. "Sit right against that post!" she says, or "Move away from the oil stove!"

* * *

Usually the Blitz is somewhere else. The wireless reports and newspaper photographs show acres of flattened East End docklands – skeletons of buildings dark against a background of furious fire, little helmeted men glistening with water from the snaking fire hoses, streets so filled with rubble that Nick wonders how the ambulances got through.

But more and more often, on his way to work in Covent Garden, the tube station at such-and-such a place is knocked out, passengers are advised to take a bus instead; and the bus ride takes him past Burtons the Tailor of Taste, Boots Cash Chemists, the ABC restaurant – places he knows well, has visited often: but this particular Burtons' smashed-in frontage displays drunken mannequins in torn suits with broken glass on their shoulders.

Or outside the ABC, there's a group of girls – the waitresses and cashiers – grouped in front of the tons of bricks, tiles and broken glass that was their workplace; and some of them are crying.

And all that remains of Boots is the word BOO, in that familiar curly script, and even that is being kicked aside by tired Rescue Squad and demolition men.

Never mind. *His* house is standing, *his* place of work has its glass windows intact. And he's a bit late again, but Mr Newton hasn't noticed, he's got away with it.

CABBAGES AND PEAS

Nick's desk is in the smallest room at the very top of Caslon Gill's play publishers, Covent Garden. His work is to record and follow up the Amateur Rights.

He had to do Amateur Rights when he worked for Jean Lang, but that was just part of his job, the dreary part. Now Amateur Rights are all. And totally boring.

You want them explained? Very well. Your amateur-dramatics group does *George and Margaret*. The performing fee is three pounds, paid through the play's publishers. Being a theatrically-minded person, the performer thinks himself rather special. High above vulgar money matters. He might get away without paying the playwright's fee. On the other hand, he puts up posters announcing the play, and the Performing Rights Society has eagle eyes... Oh well, he'll write a begging letter. "Dear Sirs, as this performance is for such a deserving charity, we feel sure that the Author will be willing to waive his fee."

In the good old days with Jean Lang, Nick could write back saying, "The Author regrets to inform you that he is not a charitable man. Send the money now or we will pursue you to the grave."

At Caslon Gill's, Amateur Rights come down to multiple-entry book-keeping. No human touch, just endless entries and figures that fill the dragging hours.

Release comes at the day's end. Nick goes downstairs to the Packing Department to type names and addresses on sticky labels for the outgoing parcels.

Books to be packed come down from the showroom and book store in a lift that creaks, rings a bell and talks. The voice is that of Nobby Newton, upstairs. The bell says "Stuff coming down, watch out"; Nobby Newton's voice gives any additional information – "Here, Vi, look sharp, get this lot out tonight, they've been on the flippin' phone complaining."

"Some people don't know there's a war on," Vi says. She tucks half a hundredweight of books under her meaty, rounded arm, and slams them down on the long packing tables. "C'mon then, Rosie," she says, "let's get this lot saucered and blowed."

Rosie is as big and round and strong-armed as Vi, but darker. She looks like a gipsy. Vi looks like a countrywoman who did well with livestock, made her pile and decided to become a Cockney. Both appear fit, rosy, even sun-tanned. Neither would stand any nonsense, thank you very much, who do you think you are, Adolf Hitler?

They work as good butchers work – fast, hard, brutally, noisily singing. Slap-slap-*thump*, and a load of books is halved and quartered into a cube. *Slap-crackle-thump-thump*, the thick brown paper forms double-seamed wraprounds with neatly pointed ears to tuck in. *Tsssur... Veep...! DACK!* and the hairy white string whips round the solid cube, half-hitches itself below, presents itself on top for the multiple knot and the flip of the hand (DACK!) that snaps the string clean. Nick has tried to do this trick but merely hurt his hands and made Vi and Rosie laugh.

But he can type. The old upright Royal spits out a label every seven seconds or so. "Go on, Blondie, play us a tune!" they shout; and he clatters out an address in rhyme. They join in: "Ah, gotcher – *Any old iron, any old iron, any any any old iron.*" They teach him dirty songs – dirty but fresh, like good compost: *Ooooooh, she sits among the cabbages and peas.* Songs with mournful tunes and ludicrous words.

They know a thousand songs, all old. He teaches them only one new one – "*Who put the Benzedrine in Mrs Murphy's Ovaltine?*" – and glows with pride in their acceptance of it.

They make Nick realize, yet again, his pig ignorance and humble status. Vi and Rosie are proper people, people known and understood by themselves and their fellows, the sort who automatically take charge in the lifeboat when the ship goes down. They are solid sticks of rock, with the lettering going all the way through.

He, by contrast, is a flimsy paper bag full of jolly jelly babies, not to be handled too much because the colours might run.

For once, the difference does not disturb him. With people like Vi and Rosie in the world – not just in the world, right next to you, calling you Blondie – the world will go on, the human race will win through.

And never mind the Nazis.

MAKING BEES LAY
Nevertheless, the Nazis must be minded.

In the cellar, his sister is asleep on a camp bed. His mother pretends to be asleep but is wide awake, listening to the bombers and the bombs. Uncle Rob is snoring with his mouth open and his upper denture plate dangling down to half-fill the black hole of his mouth. Nick is wondering whether to get up

and do a pee in the Elsan toilet (but it makes a ping-
ing, rattling noise) before the bombers come any
nearer.

Tonight, they are far too close. The sky pulses
with them, the ground quivers with high-explosive
messages from not far away; the flames of the oil
stove and a candle flicker nervously.

Then suddenly – hell, you can't mean it! – *bash,
crash, smash*, our ack-ack guns, they must have
stuck a whole nest of them just round the corner,
never heard them so loud.

And rattles and scrapes as pieces of their shrapnel
rain down, and someone's greenhouse cops it, that's
the shrill tinkle of glass.

And OOOM, OOOOMER OOM-OOOM, OOOOM, they're
right above our heads, you can hear engine noises
you don't normally hear, exhausts?

And *EEEEEEE … CRASH! EEEEE … CRASH!* and the
floor jumps upward.

Everyone's suddenly making stupid panicky little
movements. "Turn the oil stove out!" One good
blow – pfff! – done it—

EEEEEEE … then, a shattering crash!

Nick's ears ring. His brain shakes, his eyes are
wonky too, everything's gone dim – no, it's dust,
mixed coal dust and plaster dust. Ma's patting at her
hair, it's gone white.

Then a fireworks-day screaming in the sky: and an
explosion so huge that eyes are driven in and ears
seem to burst and the candle jumps sideways and
goes out –

And the sound of the house coming down, a long
drawn-out sound, a multiple sound of timbers split-

ting, bricks tumbling, tables sliding, glass shattering, teacups tinkling ... and over all, that heaving,
rumbling, sliding, weighty sound that means that it
can happen to him, it has happened to him.

Buried alive.

Nothing of the sort. "We can get out, look, the
wooden cellar steps are still OK, I'll go up first
because I'm the lightest... No, honestly, they feel
solid as a rock. Look, I've got the door open, I can
get into the kitchen hallway! I'm in!" (God, what a
mess, I can see the sky through what was the kitchen
wall, the dresser's on the floor, everything's broken,
it's worse than the films...)

"Yes, throw us the rope. Hang on to it as you
come up the steps, just in case. But honestly, the
steps are OK, perfectly safe."

The stink of plaster dust: the clean chill of the
night air. (Gas, what about gas? Can't smell it.
Here's the mains tap, turn ... it ... *off*.)

God, the mess...

This is *my* home, you can't do this to me!

An air-raid warden, a decent middle-aged man who
does his best to be sympathetic – but he has seen it
all before – stands with Nick at the bottom of the
long, narrow garden.

"Sorted your mum out as best I can about com-
pensation and claims and all that," says the warden,
"but of course it all takes time, there being a war
on."

"A war on," echoes Nick.

"Trouble is," says the warden, "the house is still

standing. I mean, not totally demolished. Not a direct hit."

"Direct hit," says Nick. In normal circumstances, the man might be offended by these repetitions. But he knows the state of the lad's mind. Shocked. Dulled. Big bang, then a big let-down.

They stare blankly at the house, which stares blankly back because all but one of its windows are missing. A huge zigzag crack runs across the back wall. The roof tiles have gone absent. "Shore it up, that's what they'll do," says the warden. "Make it habitable."

"Habitable," says Nick.

Habitable! With his father's big *Madame Butterfly* picture, the one that got accepted for the Royal Academy, split right across! With the kitchen like one of those Breaking Up the Happy Home pantomime sketches, all smashed crockery and shattered glass! Habitable, with, in his mother's sitting room, a knife-thrower's act of glass daggers forming a perfect rectangle in the wall facing the window!

Dully, he notices that all the cabbages from the cabbage patch have flown up into the pear tree; and all the pears are now lying in the cabbage patch. This is funny, he ought to laugh.

"Keep bees, then?" the warden says.

Nick nods. There's the beehive. It has been lifted up bodily by the blast of the bomb and has landed some twelve feet away, still on its legs. But the bees are baffled. They mill around like an untidy swarm over the place where the hive ought to be.

They silently watch the bees for a long time. Buzz, buzz, buzz. Then the warden gravely says, "That should make 'em lay!"

Nick finds himself roaring with laughter, helpless with it.

Nick's treasured wooden-boxed Meccano set, given him by the doctor across the road ... gone. His sister's precious Danish doll with knitted clothes and a pompon hat – gone. The collection of Grandpa's coins, very valuable – gone. Scattered by the blast? Vaporized? Never mind how. They're gone.

But the electricity is on, so is the gas. Tea can be made, meals cooked. He goes to his mother's sitting room with the Hoover, connects the special exhaust tube, hangs it out of the window, switches on and starts hoovering up the powdered glass and plaster that covers the floor. Clever stuff, this! See the plume of dusty muck spouting out into the open air! Good lad, keep at it.

He is amazed when the door is flung open and his mother is there, wild-eyed, tear-streaked, furious. "Will you *stop* that *dreadful* noise!" she shouts. "How *can* you be so selfish?"

They stare at each other, she frantic, he amazed. Then her face crumbles. "I have one of my headaches coming on," she says. "I think I will have a little lie-down."

Nick has sense enough to see that his mother has lost a bit more than Meccano, coins, dolls; she is crying out for Normality, the old routines, even the old headaches.

He sees her to her bedroom and for once fetches her pills without being asked.

FOUR

WEATHER EYE

Nick is getting older. He is eighteen, nineteen. And the World War is two.

Somehow, Nick finds himself playing the part of Meteorological Officer (Probationary).

He undergoes a training course in the West Country.

He learns about Synoptic Charts – maps of Britain to be filled in every three or four hours with coded reports from airfields and weather stations all over the place. To fill in the chart, he is taught the codes denoting the amounts of low, medium and high cloud, wind direction and speed, precipitation, barometric pressure, visibility and much else.

Two pens are used to fill in the charts. One pen uses red, the other black, ink. They are bound together at the nib ends. He writes one plain, one purl, tinily and neatly, around a circle representing the place the particular report came from – almost always an airfield.

All the reports come pouring in through a chattering teleprinter. The report he has helped prepare is also transmitted by the teleprinter, which is like a typewriter electrically connected to thousands of identical typewriters via a headquarters.

He knows from the first – from the very atmosphere of the training school, from the voices and faces of the instructors and other trainees – that meteorology will not be his mission in life, his vocation, his Guiding Star. But it has advantages: it fills the gap between being a civilian and being called up. It gets him into the wartime scene – on to RAF airfields. And it might give him some part, however minor, in the War.

Obviously the War cannot be ignored. He cannot simply say "I'm not playing." Already he has been through the Blitz – seen his sister facing call-up (she becomes a Wren, a Navy girl) – and has been blasted out of London by enemy action; the bomb shook his Victorian-suburban home so badly that it was declared unsafe. Now the family home is a small rented house in a dull Sussex seaside village.

Just as obviously, the War is here to stay. Hitler has blitzkrieged France, Belgium, Poland, Denmark, Holland, Norway – pretty well everywhere that matters from north Africa to the Norwegian fjords. Italy and various eastern European and neutral countries are his declared or undeclared allies. He is winning hands down.

But mighty America is our friend. America sends war materials, food, money, ships, vehicles and good wishes. Unfortunately, America is three thousand miles away – and lavishly at peace. The American stars and stripes have never waved so radiantly. The Union Jack is hanging in tatters.

However, Britain has escaped a Nazi invasion. In

1940, Hitler had his troop-carrying barges ready. He sent his bomber aircraft to soften up our beaches and defences. Our Hurricanes and Spitfires and radar stations proved – amazingly – to be too much for them. The RAF wins the Battle of Britain, the battle that prevented a sea invasion. "Never in the course of human conflict," Churchill says, "has so much been owed by so many to so few."

The words ring true, then and now.

Nick is assigned to an airfield near his new Sussex home. This is done because he is "on probation" as a Met Officer. A posting near home simplifies sacking him if he fails.

The airfield is well known to him. In peacetime, it was a fun aerodrome, a place for pleasure flights and MGs carrying cheery young men and blondes in headscarves.

It has changed little. You could hardly call it "operational". Its main RAF exhibit is a Walrus, an ancient biplane seaplane with a single fat engine mounted up high. It is used for air-sea rescue. It toddles off to find and pull aboard aircrews shot down "in the drink". It is a dear old thing, a sort of aerial nanny.

In the Met office, there is a teleprinter, telephone, chairs and desks. Outside, there is a slatted box, the Stevenson screen, holding the usual wet and dry thermometers to measure air-humidity and so on. On the ground there is a rain gauge and on the roof a crystal-ball sunshine recorder and the mast of the pressure-tube anemometer, which tells how the wind is blowing.

Regularly, Nick helps inflate and send up big hydrogen balloons. Released, these sail fatly into the sky. Nick follows them with a tripod-mounted theodolite, shouting out at intervals the direction and height of the balloon. This tells how the upper winds are blowing. It is enjoyable.

Still more enjoyable is the bar-billiards table, a peacetime survivor. Nick spends as much time as possible avoiding the mushrooms – particularly the black one – on the table. But he is seldom able to beat his oppo, a Welshman, who one day says, "I've got tickets for the Cup Final." (Who played whom that year? Who won...? But it was a great day out. Football hooligans had not yet been invented.)

BUSINESS MATTERS
Nick settles into the office routine.

He cycles from home to work; follows the strictly laid-down procedures; then cycles home again, past cows in fields bounded by flintstone walls, then along the coast road, past railway-carriage bungalows and rickety holiday homes. One shabby little house is called *I Dunno*; its neighbour, *I Do*.

Beyond lies his lifetime friend, the sea, which used to welcome his childhood shrimping net, his youthful beach canoe, his first "wild" night-time beach parties with driftwood bonfire flaring, girls squeaking and hooting.

"I jolly well *won't* go in, it's simply *freezing*!"

"Oh, come on, be a sport, I dare you!"

"Beast! Stop pulling at me, I *won't* go in!"

Screams, splashes, firelit limbs, phosphorescent water...

But now the friendly sea is forbidden territory, cut off with lines of square concrete cubes and garlanded with unending loops of barbed wire. The very stones and shingles are mined. All in honour of Hitler.

Home, airfield. Airfield, home. A routine. Nick doesn't much mind. The War becomes a continuing fact of life, a sort of unending winter.

Yet sometimes there are dramatic, stormy passages.

Farther along the coast, his sister – now a Wren officer in a smashing little tricorn hat – is stationed at a port which is a naval base. The German bombers attack it. Not regularly, but intensively.

From his bedroom window, Nick sees the glow of the fires and sometimes hears the dull thunder of the bomb explosions. To him, this is nothing very serious: they can't possibly do anything to his sister – she is, like himself, immune to death.

To his mother, the threat is real and nightmarish. He sees her body tensing in the cushioned armchair, her face grow suddenly weak and old, her eyes flicker with fear. "Oh, come on, Ma, she'll be all right, honestly."

He feels almost impatient with his mother's anxiety.

At the airfield, a real warplane lands – a Spitfire!

It comes in fast. It is somehow heroic. The Perspex hatch goes back, the pilot eases himself out. The pilot is not heroic. He is dark, small, bareheaded, bad-tempered. He holds a cigarette and makes accusing gestures with his leather-clad free arm. The petrol bowser trundles up, the nozzle of a hose is stuck into one wing (the pilot keeps smoking), papers are signed, the Rolls-Royce Merlin engine roars, the Spitfire is gone.

And that is all. Why does it stick in Nick's mind? Almost certainly because this was business. The pilot was engaged in some sort of war business. The Spitfire was a vicious, elegant, businesslike war machine.

Oh well, back to the Synoptic Charts and the two scratchy pens held together with a rubber band. It's not *my* business, Nick thinks. Not yet, anyhow, Probably never.

ENEMY ACTION

There are night shifts in the Met Office because weather changes its mind twenty-four hours a day; and because at any time, a pilot may want to know the QFE – the barometric pressure at the airfield where he intends to make a landing. Given the QFE, a pilot can reset his altimeter to his exact height and land on the ground instead of smashing into it or floating above it into limbo.

One night, in the middle of stating a QFE, there is a hideous bang somewhere out there in the dark and the ceiling falls in on Nick. Then the door is blown in.

More bangs! Nick makes his escape, rushing down the staircase, through the falling dust and broken glass, into the open air.

A final *whoomf!* – then the grating bellow of engines at full throttle – and it's all over, the

German pilot has belted off over the Channel, heading for home. Probably he had bombs left over from a more serious raid and thought this little airfield as good a place as any to get rid of them.

Nick has a torch. Its beam shows the Stevenson screen, that smugly tidy little slatted box, leaning lopsided on its stand. Inside it, the thermometers and other devices are all broken. Something over there in the darkness – a hut, a tractor? – is ablaze and the fire-engine is bouncing across the moonlit grass.

Back in the office, he tries the teleprinter. It is still working. A synoptic hour is coming up: he must complete his readings, which are coded into a string of five-number groups.

Tonight, there are question marks within the groups. He types: *Report incomplete owing to enemy action.*

It gives him great satisfaction.

MEDICAL MATTERS

A greater satisfaction comes from a medical student in the nearby town.

She has wings of dark hair, warm eyes and an oval face in the Botticelli style. Nick met her at a town hall dance, a posh affair for which he brushed his three pound Burton suit. He hates dancing and despises the dance band musicians – wobbling saxes, sagging rhythm sections, rinky-tinky pianists – but goes to dances because girls do.

Most of the girls are either awful or firmly attached to someone. Just sometimes, however, a radiant girl is spotted floating two or three feet above the crowd like the fairy on a Christmas tree. Such a girl is Anita.

The "Paul Jones" gives him access to her. A "Paul Jones" occurs when the band stops making a mess of some American standard and begins making a mess of "Here We Go Round the Mulberry Bush". At this signal, the dancers form two concentric, hand-in-hand rings, girls inside, turning in opposite directions. Suddenly the music stops. The couples who happen to be facing each other become temporary dance partners. Whom you end up with is a matter of chance.

But the "Paul Jones" can be fixed by a determined man. Nick joins the outer ring of males, but gives the appearance of not knowing what he is doing. He hovers and havers. He is both inside and outside the ring. And so, when the rimshot and cymbal sound the "Halt!" signal, he manages to dart at the chosen girl – flash a quick, idiot smile at the man who should have got her – and dance off with his prize, Anita.

He is lucky. Anita is one of a big party, she is unattached. Luckier still, he makes her laugh when the band plays *I'm the Sheikh of Araby ... your heart belongs to me ... each night when you're asleep ... into your tent I creep*. His funny joke, picked up from bored jazz musicians forced to play dance dates, is to repeat the phrase *With no pants on* between each of the lines of the song.

Anita laughs. Nick keeps a firm hold on her, dances again and again with her. The last waltz is announced. The band slobbers through it. *Who's taking you home tonight, whisp'ring "Darling I love you, I do", Who's the lucky boy who's going*

your way, to kiss you goodnight in your doorway?
He says, "May I see you home?" She says, "Fine, I'll
just tell the others." She is his!

Then – *miracolo!* – her shoes are agony. "Can we
sit down for a moment?"

"Yes, over there, that park bench."

He tries to take advantage. She laughs smoothly
and lets him. She is even helpful about difficulties
with lingerie.

He meets her as often as he can afford to. A min-
imum of ten shillings is necessary to buy her food
and drinks. This is a huge sum, but pride forbids
him to admit that he is always broke. He saves up.

She is kind. Although years older than Nick, and
a serious person – a medical student – she treats him
as an equal. She lets him have his way. She listens
to his Duke Ellington record of "Concerto for
Cootie" and likes it. She introduces him to the
lonely, drifting voice of Maxine Sullivan singing
"Loch Lomond". Scotch on New York rocks... And
while the music plays, she allows him to snare her
on the sofa and tamper with her person.

So he "tampers with her person". How far does
this tampering go? What are the Rules of the Game
in Nick's young days? The answer is – very different. The Pill has yet to be invented. An unmarried
mother is something of a scandal; a pregnant school-
girl, a horrifying disgrace. So it is the girl who sets
the pace and limits of an affair. The boy accepts her
rulings. He understands that girls are "courted" –
entertained at his expense. In return, she may allow
kisses, caresses, even "petting sessions".

Much later in the relationship, the girl may

suggest going Dutch Treat (sharing expenses); or allow Heavy Petting (which is Everything But). So, by later standards, Nick is not a Stud. But this is nothing to complain about. He is happy with the current Rules of the Game.

IN A MESS

It is all too good to last. Nick is posted. No longer a probationer, he is a real Met Officer, lowest grade. He is sent to an airfield in Kent.

At once the War becomes real, immediate and dramatic. The airfield is a sort of Clapham Junction: a terminus for Wellington and Blenheim bombers, a traffic centre for every kind of fighter, a target for enemy marauders.

"You can use the Sergeant's Mess, although you're a civilian," Nick is told. "You'll be all right as long as you keep your mouth shut."

Good advice. The Mess is like an annexe to a slaughterhouse. The fliers – Observers, Flight Engineers, Bomb Aimers, Air Gunners, Pilots – are all candidates for aerial slaughter. Nick has a cot to himself in a small room. Aircrew double up in their larger rooms. Their fur-lined leather jackets and Sidcot inner suits, their helmets and goggles, their photographs from home, are flung all over the place. They get shell eggs for breakfast.

They speak a foreign language that Nick instantly picks up, as does the civilian population at large. "Wizard" or "Good show" or "Bang on" means good; "Duff" or "Naff" or "a bind" means bad. "Gen" is information, "Prang" means to crash or be crashed, "Ops" are operations.

The language avoids heroics. Nick asks, "Where's Sammy? He was going to give me a game of pills."

"Sammy? He's bought it, didn't you know? Got hit. Gone for a Burton."

This means, "Sammy was killed, he is dead."

Heroics are reserved for the unheroic. Someone may tell Nick, "Don't waste your time talking to Taffy, he won't hear you. Been shot down in flames."

"By whom?"

"Some blonde bint. Smashing bit of crumpet."

Translation: Taffy has fallen for a bint, a piece of crumpet or homework – a girl; and it is serious, he has been "shot down in flames".

Aircrew are young men. You are old at thirty. To Nick, the Flight Sergeant called "Uncle" is wonderfully old: he is thirty-two, a joke age. Everyone is in their twenties. Nick is only a teenager, which is *too* young. But the men, the real men, do more than tolerate him. He isn't their intimate, their buddy, but he is acceptable. Though only a kid, and a civilian at that, he is an OK oddity of the War. "Want a game of pills?" "Want me to beat you at chess?"

He keeps his mouth shut and his ears open, and learns silently to accept that the wizard ex-journalist who checkmated him last night has himself been checkmated today. He has bought it.

Oh well, press on regardless.

Nick sees so many new things. Standing on the little platform above the Met hut, he encounters May-bugs – insects like coarse bumble bees. They fly blind, apparently. They emit a low-pitched drone and smack straight into your eye or ear.

He sees a Wimpey, a Wellington bomber – the twin-engined job with its ingenious, geodetic, lattice-work frame covered in fabric – lurch in to land with one engine on fire and nearly all its tail missing. The remains flutter like flayed skin. Inside the fuselage, there is chaos and carnage. He runs to help but is pushed back. "Out of the way, sonny, out of the way." He obeys, bitterly aware that he *would* have been in the way.

He sees Blenheim fighter-bombers pockmarked all over with gashes and holes. The job of these aircraft is to attack enemy shipping in the Channel. The Blenheims go in very low at top speed through curtains of flak – the Germans have developed special flak ships. Nick wonders what prayers the bomb-aimers use as, protected by a few sheets of Perspex, they hurtle through the flying metal. Whatever the prayers are, they don't work too well. Losses are constant and appalling. There are Me109 fighters as well as flak ships. It isn't fair...

He sees the effect of bullets on wet earth when he is innocently cycling towards the Met hut and a Me109 (no, perhaps two or three, it is all very confusing) beat up the airfield, trying to destroy aircraft on the ground. The 109s seem to him to go faster than any aircraft ever known. That is because they fly so low, full throttle, guns blazing. And ugly with it – squared-off wing tips, big, brutal spinners, alien camouflage, black crosses. These impressions crowd in on him in seconds. Then he falls off his bicycle and lies flat on the ground, still looking up at the 109s, so low, so fast, so deadly determined.

And one of them is coming straight at him!

Unbelievable! It's like the films! It's roaring straight at him, him personally, only feet above the ground, wings tilting, firing guns!

That is when he sees the effects of bullets on wet earth. Soil and grass lift and pucker. He thinks of his mother's sewing machine: it is rather like that, lines of stitches, the material nipped and puckered, the needle darting and dabbing...

It is all over. "Here's mud in your eye," he says, and uses his dirty handkerchief to remove it. The earth had spat at him. He looks around him. There is not a lot to see, just a number of aircraft taking off in a hurry. But too late. What damage did the 109s do? A fire over there, a Warrant Officer yelling at a crowd of airmen who are milling about with fire extinguishers, a yellow Miles Magister that has become the private property of a Wing Commander making a demure landing...

Nick gets on his bicycle and goes on his way, unmoved, unterrified, unmarked. He is of course immune. No bomb or bullet has his number on it.

All the same, when that Me109 came straight at him...

His great ambition is to go for a ride in an RAF plane.

He eavesdrops on the aircrew talk in the Sergeants' Mess.

"The Blenheim hasn't a chance against—"

"The Beaufighter, now, that's a different proposition—"

"I've actually *flown* a Gladiator, all right, laugh, but it goes up like a lift."

"The Spit's nice, but not as strong as the—"

"Bloody Havocs, their exhausts fall off—"

A Sergeant Pilot, a jazz fan who doesn't give a damn about service bullshit, says, "All right, you can be freight, we've got to deliver a kite at so-and-so and we can get into town within an hour from there. You get me into the clubs, I'll give you a lift."

They take off in the dark in a Havoc, an American bomber painted all-black. Nick crouches somewhere near the middle, dazzled and delighted. The engines roar, he feels the wheels thump and bump across the field, the airframe heaves, the wings begin to lift.

A horrible noise, all wrong, a searing, tearing racket! – then thump-bump-squeal, we're slowing right down, the wheels are grinding the ground.

And at last, motionless silence broken by the voice of the pilot. "Bloody Havocs," he says. "The exhaust's fallen off."

Very occasionally, Nick gets to London. The place is changed. At night, the lights go out. In the daytime, it is grimmer, darker, dirtier. If it smiled, it would show a gap-toothed grimace. Most faces and eyes are wary and tired. Women wear boots, headscarves and slacks. Their hair is often done in a Victory Roll, a ring formed round a piece of tape.

Everything is in Short Supply or Under the Counter. "Don't you know there's a war on?" is the stock reply to a request for a particular brand of tobacco. "But I can see a tin of it there, on that shelf." "Ah, that's for my regulars. Regular customers only."

June 1941. Hitler, often portrayed by British cartoonists as a carpet-biting maniac, has invaded Russia. *Invaded Russia!* – The vast country whose winter reduced Napoleon to tears! You don't invade Russia, any more than you pick bar-room fights with heavyweight boxers.

Perhaps Hitler really does bite carpets? Perhaps he will waste so much strength on Russia that we will win the war?

Later in 1941 – tiny Japan declares war on huge America by sending bombers to cripple the US Pacific Fleet lying at anchor in Pearl Harbour.

Which means that America must now declare war on Germany. Because Japan is allied to Germany.

Surely now, with the USA on our side, we *must* eventually win the war?

AND OVER HERE
Our new American allies have invaded, sweeping all before them. Particularly Piccadilly, the taxis and the chicks.

At first, they delight Nick. Real American voices, chewing gum, ten-cent cigars! Snazzy uniforms of shiny golden-tan drill! Beautiful brown shoes instead of hobnailed black boots!

And above all, those medals. He gapes when first he stands alongside a Yank in a tube train; the man must be a hero, he's got tricky little medals hanging down in festoons!

Only later does he get close enough actually to read the medals. This medal says DRIVER, that one says COOK, the other says LATRINE ATTENDANT or whatever.

Only much later does he grow tired of the Yanks lurking in dark Piccadilly doorways chewing unlit cigars. "How's the old box, babe?" they mutter at every passing female shape. "How's the old box, babe? How's the old..."

What really hurts him is the fact that so many beautiful chicks fall for this line. Some fall two at a time, one for each American arm.

It isn't fair.

The Yanks are everywhere. Piccadilly is always crowded with them. In the underground station, they glumly queue for the telephones, then light up when they get through. "Hi, honey! Yeah, it's Hank! Now, how's about..."

They commandeer all the taxis. They can afford them. "Overpaid, overdressed, oversexed and over here." Should they be hated? Perhaps some older people do hate them. Young people don't: the Yanks are friendly, generous, open, responsive.

Beyond everything, they are not war-damaged. They haven't acquired the grey patina of their host country. They are still fresh.

Throughout Britain, kids cry, "Got any gum, chum?"

"Sorry, kid, fresh out of gum. Here, grab hold, try a Hershey bar." Smiles all round. And the smiles aren't forced.

In the jazz clubs, the Yanks bring the latest records and new life. Stunned musicians try out riffs from the Benny Goodman small groups. Nick copies Charlie Christian note for note, but it never sounds right. And nobody can hit a beat like Count Basie's rhythm section; no one can begin to imitate the suave savagery of Ellington's "Cotton Tail". American films, songs, stars, make war-worn Britain seem still more pallid. But they also cheer people up. There is a never-ending queue for *Gone with the Wind*.

MO'S POINT

There is the other side of the coin – the reaction of the Yanks to Europe's offerings. A Yank corporal, Mo, visits Nick's mother in the little Sussex house. He comes loaded with Spam, ham, lamb, jam, Lucky Strikes, stockings, all the wonderful things she has almost forgotten. Mo is twenty-one and a culture fiend. After the war, he's quitting the hardware business, he's going to paint, y'know?

He stares at Nick's father's paintings with the wonder Nick feels for Charlie Christian; then shakes his head and says, "I guess, first, you've got to learn to *draw*."

"Here's someone who could draw. Take a look. Albrecht Dürer, German. Etchings. He painted as well."

Mo takes the book and studies "Knight, Death and Devil", shaking his head slowly. He turns the pages and mutters, "Well, I mean…!"

At last he says, "When did this guy do all this stuff?"

"You can see the date there in that tablet he drew with his initials on it. 'AD' for Albrecht Dürer, then the date inside: 1407."

Mo laughs. "You're kidding. 1407, that's not possible! Nobody could do that stuff *five hundred years ago*!"

Nick thinks this over. Mo has got a point. Then and now, ancient and modern… There is, today, no artist to rival Dürer or da Vinci or Titian – or is there? No furniture-makers to rival Chippendale, no architects to rival Wren, no house-builders to approach the Georgians – or are there?

But then, what words might Shakespeare use if you took him for a fast run in a Rolls-Bentley? What would Chippendale make of the lines and technology of a Spitfire? How would Titian react to a really good movie? – would he throw away his brushes and say "Get me a moving-picture camera!"?

All around Nick, ancient and beautiful things are being smashed to powder (but the ancients, too, were enthusiastic vandals). Anywhere about him, certain men and women are planning a future of – what? Bakelite? Viscose rayon? Reconstituted marble? Perspex? Spam? Will there ever be another Great Plague, destroying millions? But isn't this war a great plague, destroying millions?

He often wonders about things like this. It does no harm. Neither does it do any good. Lofty thoughts can't produce a banana or a Mars bar.

Nick visits home whenever possible. "Lunch," announces his mother glumly, "will be at twenty past one." Hurray, whoopee, what fun.

But then there is her efficiency: how does she conjure good meals out of the tiny rations? There is her stoicism: hasn't she been through all this before during the 1914-18 war and mustn't she be sick to the back teeth with it? And her constancy: she still does things her way, she won't let Hitler interfere. "Nicholas, would you run upstairs and get my pills from my bedside table?" The same old pill routine, the same martyred, doom-laden voice.

How is it that she attracts so many interesting people: a Viennese doctor who still sends her flowers and expensive delicacies, a notable book illustrator, a flamboyant woman concert-pianist … even the Frenchwoman two doors down the ugly little road, Mrs Foucauld? You can hear her hoarse Gallic voice in the next village. She out-screeches low-flying Spitfires.

"What ees thees, no meeelk? 'Ow there ees no meelk, no cheeses, no anytheeng?"

"Sorry love, there's a war on."

"Warrr! Is not warrr I'm needing, iss meeeelk!"

It is to Nick's mother that Mrs Foucauld comes on the great day when the French are named the Fighting French.

"Aaaah, Meessis Feesk, soch great news! I 'ear heem on the raddio!"

"What news, Mrs Foucauld?"

"Oh, so terrifeek! Now we are *ze farting French*!"

To get away from the little house, Nick rides his bike to Worthing, Brighton, anywhere. Or he takes the bus, sitting on the smelly top floor so that he can smoke his pipe.

To one side there is the forbidden sea, cordoned off with square concrete blocks and barbed wire. The sea looks patient, permanent, disdainful: "Do what you like, you can't change *me*." Seagulls wheel and scream agreement, flying where they will, ignoring all barriers.

To the other side are the bungalows and houses. They look older and more tired through lack of paint.

But some gardens are still kept up. One is a

miracle of sweeping lawns and disciplined borders glowing with blooms.

Two nice ladies in ridiculous hats sit behind Nick. "Oh!" says one, seeing the garden, "oh, how sweetly pretty!"

"Yes indeed!" says the other. "*Just* like a nursing home!"

Suddenly there is a rattling noise (has the bus's engine thrown a big-end?) and a dark shape is out there, flying low over the sea, so close that you can see the crosses on the fuselage and the shape of the observer's head and shoulders in the glazed nose cone. Junkers 88! And behind it a Hurricane, guns firing.

The Ju 88 wheels away, the blatter of its engines rattling the windows of the bus. The Hurricane tilts and swings after it, showing its pale underbelly. Both aircraft are hitting some three hundred miles per hour. In seconds, they are gone.

"*Well!*" says one of the ladies. She is deeply shocked and offended by the noise and disturbance. "Well, *really!*"

The other lady has lost interest. She is staring inland again, looking at the gardens.

"They say you can save flower seeds," she says at last. "But I'm not quite sure."

GERRIM KILLIM
Brighton is joyless and tatty now. No Max Miller ("That's a nasty cough, Lady! Chesty! You want to rub it lady, give it a good rub! 'Ere, *Vic!*"), no deck chairs filled with sweaty mums and dads, no Brighton Rock, no bum-and-bosom naughty post-cards, nothing very much.

Nick somehow gets into the Royal Pavilion, the mad and wonderful folly of George IV – "as if the Taj Mahal had come to Brighton and pupped". Now the mock-Chinese furnishings, the oriental gilded ceilings, the domes and hanging dragons, fading and dusty, exotic draperies have fallen in swathes; the enormous banqueting table is laid with two tea mugs and a month-old newspaper.

He gets out before the depression of the place grips him; has a beer in the Ship; walks through the streets that used to be thronged with trippers, ice-hockey fans, boozers, shady ladies, antique shops; and begins to plod along the sea front, the promenade.

It grows dark. Ahead, he dimly sees a cluster of moving bodies and one or two torchlights swinging about. The wardens won't like that... What's going on?

A fight. A ring of men, some thirty or forty of them: and in its centre, two men, one small and hard, the other thickly plump, hitting each other. Their arms are bare. Their coats are held by ringsiders. The torches provide the only light.

"Aaaah!" the ringsiders snarl. "Grah! Yeah, yah, gerrim!"

A zoo language, a noise rising from the guts and grating through tightened throats.

"Knock his fuggin' eyes out! Fuggin' killim!"

A gang fight. Nothing to do with servicemen; something to do with the old pre-war racecourse gangs. Obviously it's organized, pre-arranged, those men are the official coat-holders and those others brought the torches.

The smaller man's mouth is split wide open at one side. You can see teeth glint through the wet red flesh. *Crack!* and my God, that's his nose broken, now there's blood pouring down his shirt, yet he stands there, eyes staring and dead, his little hard fists jabbing out, not yielding an inch.

"Garn, smashis bleedin' face in. Garn, garn!"

The thick, plump arms go left right left right, like pistons, and the heavy fists jerk the smaller man's head. Blood droplets fly.

"Thassaway, fuggin' lovely."

"Go f'ris eyes, blind the bleeder."

The little man has been waiting. Quick as a ferret, he moves inside the pumping fists and kicks upwards, just once. The bigger man screams and falls down writhing. The small man takes aim and kicks him in the mouth. The bigger man bubbles.

Half the crowd cheers and crows. Someone from the other half comes up behind the little man and hits him from behind, in the neck. The little man staggers, blunders into the crowd, spins, reels, and falls flat on his face, senseless.

Silence: then, "Giss a hand, gettem out."

"Yeah, gerrem out. Don't want no trouble."

"Catch hold 'is 'ead, I got 'is feet."

Movement, hustling, grunting, footsteps – and suddenly everyone is gone, all that's left is darkly glinting wet patches. And from a distance, an occasional low laugh.

Nick is sick over the promenade railings.

* * *

Evil.

That was *evil*. The real thing, the genuine article. Nick has been thoroughly sick and now he is chilled to the marrow. Evil...

> *By the shade of the old apple tree*
> *Where Hackenschmidt wrestled with me.*
> *He gave me a punch*
> *That brought up my lunch*
> *And threatened my dinner and tea.*

That's not evil. The Three Stooges, Tom and Jerry, professional boxers knocking each other out – they're not evil, however violent.

But that *was* evil. Why?

Aircrew in the Sergeants' Mess, lolling about in flying gear, flicking through magazines, waiting for the next briefing. Then, take-off, the long, cold flight, the Bomb Aimer crawling forward, taking over – "Port, Skipper, a bit more, that's it, hold it there, hold it, hold it..."

And the plane jumps upwards as the bombs are released, thousands of pounds of them, thousands of £££s of them, they scream down into the heart of what is already a Chamber of Horrors.

> *Coming in on a wing and a prayer.*
> *Coming in on a wing and a prayer.*
> *With a full crew aboard*
> *And our trust in the Lord*
> *Coming in on a wing and a prayer.*

"Our trust in the Lord." So it can't be evil.

What a scrap! What a fight!
Yes, we certainly hit our target for tonight!

Wizard, bang on, jolly good show! And if you're soldiers, the Bishop blesses you as you go overseas.

So it can't be evil. It's not the same thing at all as the fight on Brighton Promenade.

Now, that was evil. Because Nick was there, right close up. And he didn't like what he saw.

But a thousand-bomber raid is different because War is different.

Isn't it?

FIVE

O-U-T, OUT

Nick is moved from the big, dramatic airfield to a much smaller one that at first sight seems to be centred on a PRU – a Photographic Reconnaissance Unit. There are Spitfires painted very pale blue, pretty as girls' toys and no more lethal: they carry no guns, only cameras. Their skins are polished smooth as a baby's. They can fly very high and very fast. Specialist tools flown by specialists.

The Met Office is only a room, not a hut. Has Nick been demoted? Is this a step down? Very probably. He is not exactly dedicated to meteorology – but then, he does everything expected of him, just what is it that he may lack?

The question nags at him. As ever, he is disturbed by his own pig ignorance. Why has this small RAF station got such a big and elaborate control room? What goes on here? PRU and what else? Why, if he intends eventually to become a writer, does he fail to be in the know, see things in depth? Where is the probing, analytical mind – the vision that will make his war memoirs essential reading for students of Second World War history?

The answer is, of course, that he is a very young

person of no importance. He recognizes this, but all the same...

He worries about his future. It is decided for him when, one icy, sunny morning, his boss – a kindly, dedicated, hardworking Scots meteorologist who has achieved Forecaster grade – says, "Let's go for a stroll."

They stroll. "Ah, look over there!" says the Scotsman, pointing at a Spitfire. "How would you fancy flying one of those?"

"What, a Mark IV?" mumbles Nick.

"A Mark V, actually," the Scotsman corrects him. Nick blushes. "Wouldn't you be better off in one of them?"

However gently opened, however soft the material, Nick knows this to be the Sack. He is being chopped. He is o-u-t, *out*.

He is not greatly surprised or deeply upset. But he does realize – and the realization chills him – that he is one step nearer call-up.

Does he or doesn't he want to join up? Nick hardly knows. He discusses it with Len, with whom he shares digs in a town not far from the airfield.

"I've got the chop," he tells Len. "From old Mac."

"Good old Mac," Len says, not listening. Then he does a double take and says, "Do you think he's going to chop me?"

Nick thinks this over and comes to the conclusion that Mac won't chop Len. But why me, Nick thinks, and not Len? Aren't I as good as Len? Aren't I one hell of a sight better? Haven't I had things published, played in the night clubs, kissed gorgeous girls? Why prefer Len to me?

That night Nick and Len queue outside the cinema to see a weepie, *Dangerous Moonlight*, in which a soulful Polish concert pianist goes blind, or paralytic, or whatever, and is held together by a soulful English actress photographed through gauze. This film introduced a highly emotional piece of music that swept the nation – "The Warsaw Concerto".

When it is all over and the usherettes are herding the audience out, Nick says, "My *gawd*. Not a dry seat in the house."

"Yes, yes, oh yes," Len says, his face as mistily poetic as the actress's. "My God indeed! Wasn't that the most beautiful piece of music you've ever heard in all your life?"

"It was a load of drivel."

"Yes, oh yes," says Len, rolling his eyes. He begins humming "Da da de-DAH DAH de DAH, de dah de DAH DAH de DAH" – the "Moonlight Sonata" theme. He is uplifted, ecstatic.

Nick spits in the gutter. "And they've sacked *me*, not *him*," he thinks, bitterly.

A PARTICULAR EXPERIENCE

Early one morning, just as the sun was rising, I saw a fair maiden in the valley below.

What brought that song into Nick's head? A girl over there, a "fair maiden". She's being pushed against the wall by a big, heavy, beery man, his body is smothering hers, his head is poked forward, hers is drawn back. She's afraid.

Well, none of my business, thinks Nick. I've got

to get on, away from this suburban pit, back to Leicester Square.

Hold on, there's something wrong. She's trying to get away from him, she's pushing at him, but she's not strong enough. And she's crying, a feeble whingeing sobbing. *How could you treat a poor maiden so?*

None of my business, happens all the time, Nick thinks. Keep moving, tube station round the corner. But I'll have to pass them to get to it.

"Please don't... Please don't..." Nick is so close that he can see her stained face, her smeared lipstick, her tangled hair. Not a very fair maiden. Not a very fair district. They copped it last night, you can smell the bomb damage and taste it too. Yeuck.

The man is old and boozy. Worse, he's a proper drunk, you can tell by the skin on his face. Millions of little broken veins, those yellow-celluloid eyes. Perhaps I ought to—

"Please don't... Please don't... I'm expected at home."

He's got her jumper pushed up. Nick can see her white midriff, such pale skin. The man's hands are inside her jumper, moving about.

Nick changes his mind. Like it or not, I've *got* to do something... "Excuse me! Excuse me, mate! Excuse me, am I going right for the tube station?" That's a safe beginning. No good saying, *Unhand that unhappy maiden, you cur.* He might turn violent. Drunks do.

No response. "The *tube station*. Am I going the right way?"

Great, he's actually turning his horrible head. What a bloated pig of a man. Pity he's twice Nick's weight.

"Gerra fugginout." He lurches at Nick, shoving his thick-fingered hand out. Nick puts the guitar down against the wall. Safe over there. He hopes.

"The tube station. Am I going the right way?"

"Gerra fugginout. Nunna your biznish. You wanna ... you wanna make trouble?"

The man curls his grey-yellow fingers into a fist and swings. The fist misses by a foot and splats against the brick wall. Blood pours from broken knuckles. He stares at it, pop-eyed with surprise. He has forgotten the girl. She slips sideways along the wall towards Nick.

"'Ere, looka this! Bleedin' blood!" says the man.

"I'm expected home," the girl repeats, weakly. She looks about to faint. Tears streak her face.

Nick carries her away with one arm, his guitar at the end of the other. The drunk still stares at his bleeding knuckles.

"I'll take you home. Where do you live?"

"Over there." She points towards broken roofs and chimneys topped with a grey-yellow dust cloud. "It's quite close," she says. She pulls out a handkerchief, wipes her eyes and nose, and says, "I've got to see to Tinker."

"Yes, Tinker," says Nick, blankly. Trying to make conversation, he says, "You're up and about good and early."

"Up late," says the girl. "Up late last night."

"You mean you haven't been to bed?" says Nick,

trying to keep things light. "Been making a night of it, eh?"

The girl nods, quite vigorously. "It went on all night," she says. "But now it's morning."

Nick is baffled. He walks, the girl keeps pace, but seems a little drunk. Her feet do not obey her head, they suddenly tend left or right.

"Was it a party?" says Nick.

"We're nearly there," the girl replies. "I've got to see to Tinker."

"That man, do you know him? Was he at the party?"

"Party?" says the girl; then laughs, uncertainly. "Some party!" she says and gives Nick a sidelong look that seems almost flirty. But her eyes are wrong, they seem starred, fractured. Then – "Home now," she says.

She points down a street and begins to make little high-pitched sucking sounds with pursed lips. "Vvvp-vvvp!" her lips say. "Vvvp-vvvp!"

SEEING TO TINKER

The street is almost demolished. Most of the houses have spilled into slopes of reeking rubble. The houses still standing are bashed and battered to jagged caricatures, with vacantly grinning crooked window frames, stumps of chimneys like mad hats; they are pantomime sets, open to the air, furnished with lavatory cisterns, suits on hangers, upside-down armchairs, collapsing stairs, an alarm clock dead centre on a little table with a glass of water beside it, a split wardrobe that has spat its clothes over the roof next door.

The wardens and rescue men have obviously finished their work long ago. Their Coventry Climax pumps are silent, their helmets mostly off. Now they drink mugs of tea from a WVS van. Some fiddle with barriers that cordon off the street.

"Number twenty-six," says the girl, almost brightly. Now she is pulling Nick along.

"Steady on, luv," a warden says. "You too, son. Can't go in, it's all sealed off."

"Number twenty-six," the girl says, shaking her head. "I live there." She walks still faster. The warden protesting has to trot to keep pace.

"Don't you think we'd better..." Nick begins. But once again the girl, smiling now, is making her little sucking sounds: "Vvvp! Vvvp-vvvp!"

She pushes aside a broken-hinged garden gate, its faded blue paint pockmarked with bomb fragments. No. 26. Still smiling, she walks through a side door into a narrow passage, the side entrance of the house. She stops to face a big kitchen window with only tiny shards of glass like babies' teeth left in the glazing bars.

"Help me up, please," she says politely. The warden and Nick are too stunned to deny her. She wants to be lifted: they put their hands on her waist and lift. She is light. "Higher, a bit higher please," she says.

She reaches it – the birdcage. It is hooked to a long ribbon tied to the curtain rail. She unhooks the cage and carefully brings it down. "Vvvp-vvvp!" she says, her head on one side, her pursed mouth smiling. "Who's a lovely boy, den? Ess, oo are! My Tinker!"

The bird lies dead on the sandy floor of the cage. Its little legs stick out like twigs. The girl beams at it.

Nick and the warden exchange looks. "You're the one who found her, then?" the man says, in an undertone.

"Yes. A short time ago. A drunk had got hold of her. He was, you know, messing her about."

The girl puts down the cage and says, "I'll get Dad's breakfast now." She fiddles with her straggled hair. "I've mislaid my comb," she says. Nick offers her his. Discreetly, she gives it a quick double wipe on her skirt before using it.

The warden mutters, "This lot happened about one o'clock. So she's been wandering about all night."

Nick says, "What about her folks?"

The warden shakes his head very slightly. All dead. He sees a WVS lady and beckons her. She comes across, he says a few words in her ear. The girl gets on with her combing. Her brown hair is springy and difficult to untangle. "That's better," she says at last, politely returning the comb to Nick. "I'll just pop the kettle on and take Dad his tea. But..."

She looks at the shattered window of the kitchen and for the first time seems puzzled. "But..." she says again. Nick feels gaping, rigid, powerless.

The WVS lady instantly takes command. She puts her arm round the girl's shoulder and, chattering incessantly, leads her away. The girl is quite content to be led. She even responds to the lady's talk. The last words Nick hears the girl say are, "He catches the 8.05, but we never know when he'll be back, poor old Dad." The WVS lady nods and nods and pilots the girl.

Nick and the warden stare at the dead bird in its cage. They can think of nothing to say for a long time. Nick asks, "What will happen to her?"

The warden says, "How should I bloody know?" Then, dourly and monotonously, he begins swearing at the War.

Nick picks up his guitar and takes the tube to Leicester Square.

Nick is miserable because of the girl with the birdcage. She fills his thoughts. What happens to her now? Where is she going to end up?

What happens to *us* now? Where will we end up?

Will we win the war? It is impossible to imagine us losing it. We're not like the damn Parleyvoos, Russkies, Spaghetti-bashers and Sausage-eaters. They are always losing wars and being invaded. We never are. Similarly, you, he or she may be killed but I won't be.

All the same, *when* will the war end? This year, next year, some time, never? Suppose it goes on long enough to turn the people in the deep shelters into owl-eyed troglodytes, unable to face the light of day? Suppose the VC-winning battlefield hero grows tired of bravery and goes into the black market? Suppose the tight-lipped war widows and widowers suddenly open their mouths and start screaming obscenities in the street?

Meanwhile, here's a mum in the shelter with the kids, knitting. "Yes, that *was* a big one, wasn't it? But never mind, here's your teddy, back to sleep." Dad is thousands of miles away – "Cripes, the bloody thing's jammed again!" – frantically clearing his Bren gun while sand or mud or ice gets into his top pocket and spoils the crumpled snapshots of the kiddies.

Here's a public-school boy who ran out of luck and was put down a coal mine.

Here's a coalminer who got lucky and brought down a Heinkel with the first rounds from the turret of a Lancaster.

Here's a rest centre for the bombed-out and bereaved: "There, dear, a nice cup of tea. Lovely. Can you tell me your name, dear? Go on, *try...*"

Here's a commercial artist with a big peacetime reputation for scraperboard illustration, at present being clubbed to death in a Japanese POW camp.

When does it stop? When do "the lights go on again ... all over the world", as the song has it? What happens when it's over? Will my mother, for instance, be taking her little rest – or arsenic?

Don't be so dramatic, Nick. What have *you* got to moan about? Here's Leicester Square. Careful with the guitar. Got your ticket? Yes. That Norwegian airman looks lost. The YMCA? Follow me. Does he understand? Yes, he's smiling. Smile back, nod your head.

Nod your head harder, you might be able to shake that girl out of it.

But she won't go away. She haunts Nick, yet he cannot clearly remember her face or what she wore — anything about her. Yet she was like someone. Someone nice.

> *She was a nice girl*
> *And I will never understand*
> *Why did she fall for the leader of the band?*

SIX

BLOOMERS

London, a year and more after the Blitz, still blacked out at night, still queueing for goods in short supply or Subject to Wartime Restrictions, still short of drinks in the pubs. *I'm going to get lit up when the lights go on in London! I'm going to get lit up as I never was before!*

Nick goes to see Judy and Gareth in their modern flat high above London. From it, Nick first saw the strangest, most beautiful sight the War offered ... the endless level field of barrage balloons; gentle, dreaming, silver gas-filled porkers.

Gareth is at the BBC. He gives talks on the Overseas Service. He is listened to all over Europe because all Europe knows that our broadcasts are not mere propaganda: they tell the truth. Not all the truth, that would be impossible; but what can be said is to be taken so seriously that, in many Nazi-occupied countries, you can be shot for tuning in to BBC wavelengths.

In Britain, the opposite is true. The Nazis have their "Lord Haw-Haw", a British renegade who is their propaganda front man. The British have to listen to him, it is a social duty. He is as good as a show. Everyone imitates his voice – "Jairmany calling, Jairmany calling" – the voice of a twentieth-century Dracula, you can almost see the bats fluttering around his head. A voice so coldly menacing, so nasty-Nazi, that people fall about with laughter hearing it.

Gareth is out, but Judy is in. "Jairmany calling," Nick says through the letterbox. Her quick footsteps come to the door – he is allowed briefly to peck her cheek – then, "Thank goodness you've come, now we can have coffee. You make it, there's a love, I'll sort out this stuff." The stuff is typescripts of articles or short stories, scattered over the dining table.

"I wish Gareth were here, I never see him and he'd love to see *you*—"

"One tablespoon of coffee, is that right?"

"Yes, that's the maximum. We'll be down to bloody acorns soon, still, I suppose it's a good thing, rationing and everything. Yet I never seem to lose any weight, *why* can't I be like her, just look at her!" She wags a woman's magazine at him. The cover shows the usual white-toothed, red-lipped, slender fashion lovely.

"You suit you as you are," says Nick.

"No I don't. The other night I'd had a bath, and I was sitting in front of the dressing-table mirror looking at myself all naked. Gareth was in bed, reading the papers, I said to him, 'Oh dear, why can't I be a *femme fatale*?'"

"Here's your coffee," Nick says.

"He didn't even look up, he just said, '*Femme fatale*? Don't worry, darling, you'll always be a *femme fatarse*!'"

Nick laughs so hard that he splutters coffee over Judy's typing. She dabs a dishcloth at the spots like a bird pecking: they are gone instantly. "What are you writing?" she says, in the matter-of-fact tone of voice that deserves an answer like, "Oh, a couple of shorts for *New Writing*, and a novel for dear old Hodders, and a critical piece or two. Rather too much on my plate actually. But one must live, hmmm?"

And she would say, "Oh, *Nick*, we had no idea...!"

In fact Nick has written little or nothing and sheepishly admits it. She nods, says, "Let's have more coffee", does something in the kitchen that causes a landslide of crockery, says, "Oh bugger!" and tells him, "We've got just the thing for you. A piece about Amelia Jenk Bloomer, you know, the American woman who invented Bloomers. Go and see the editor of – hang on, I'll write down the details."

She does so. He writes, groans, rewrites and finally finishes the piece. It is published. His name is in print in a first-rate magazine.

He stares at the published pages and says, "That's *me*, I did that."

Or was it O'Leary?

O'LEARY SAYS

O'Leary is a children's game. One child takes a turn of being in charge. He or she stands in front of the others, who are lined up like soldiers. The leader gives commands.

"O'Leary says, hop up and down on one foot."
The children hop up and down.
"O'Leary says, hop on the other foot."
They obey.
"O'Leary says, rub your noses."
They hop and rub their noses.
"Stop!"
A few of the children fall for it: they stop. But they shouldn't have done, you obey only those commands beginning with the name "O'Leary". The losers drop out, the winners continue to obey O'Leary's commands.

You do something only when O'Leary gives the word.

Nick is like that. Someone else, never himself, gets him going. There always has to be an O'Leary acting as his starter motor.

Judy and Gareth O'Learied his "Bloomers" article. Freddie got him into the jazz-club scene. He was pushed into the Met Office.

Mags took charge when, filled with guilt about his attempts at her seduction, he proposed marriage (while making it quite clear that it is impossible, he is only a teenager, he hasn't any money and anyway he'll soon be called up).

That had been in Kent, just after the outbreak of war, when Nick had left school and did not know what to do with himself. So he was packed off to Kent for a holiday with family friends, the Blounts.

"Kent, sir — everybody knows Kent — apples, cherries, hops, and women." Or did Mr Jingle say "pretty women"? He should have done.

Mags, the youngest Blount daughter, was pretty. Pretty, athletic, sure of herself, happy. And just Nick's age.

It was a large family devoted to show spaniels, Rex rabbits, best of breed rosettes, chickens, vegetables and war with the carrion crows. The father was a painter and musician who was forced to surrender his talents to a life in gumboots. He didn't seem bitter about this, just distant and very quiet.

His wife was a virago, a shrew, a gumbooted raver with furiously glaring blue eyes and spikes and tufts of grey-white hair that flew from her head like exclamation marks. She stumped and thumped, she brandished swill buckets, she flung the latest baby-chicken corpses (the carrion crowns got them) in Nick's face. "My God! – have I got to do *everything*? Get the bloody shot gun! Hide your useless self in that henhouse and don't come out till you've killed the murdering swine!"

Nick slunk to the henhouse. Inside it, what little air there was was filled with stinking dust. Exactly out of range, the hunch-backed crows had poked their cruel whiskered beaks at him and knowingly bobbed their heads. They bounced about and flaunted their ragged feathers. They'd croaked sneeringly – "Caw, blimey, you think we don't know you're there? Caw, caw, haw-haw!"

Nick never got a crow. He got spots down his back from the poisonous dust.

In the night when, please God, everyone was asleep, and Mags was beside him on the narrow but blissful bed, they'd kissed to the music of Kentish nightingales. Then she'd rubbed his spots with Germolene.

Mags listened to his proposal smiling mildly. Then she pushed a handful of sticky-weed down the neck of his shirt and ran away laughing.

When he caught her, she fell back on the grass and put her arms around his neck. "You really are nice," she said, giving him an elder-sister sort of kiss.

O'Leary again. She had taken charge, she set the tone and pace. She also informed him, kindly, that there are two people involved in lovey-dovey games — and the smaller and softer of the two might be the O'Leary.

She also beat him at tennis when they played on the decaying public courts. She was naturally athletic. Her backhand was a graceful sweep; his an anxious scramble. Her service was a *pang*, his a twang. "Game, set *and* match!" she said, throwing her racket up in the air and catching it. "Shall we pack it in?"

O'Leary wins, six games to three. So? It's only a game of tennis with a smashing girl. He doesn't care who wins or loses.

But perhaps he should?

Time goes by, the war goes on. By now, early 1943, the war game seems to be turning out something like the tennis: about six games to three, our side winning.

The Germans have lost the desert war in North Africa. Rommel, the German General, seemed an indomitable, superman figure — dark-goggled, hard as nails, as coldly efficient as his Tiger tanks. But our Montgomery, last and most quirkily British of a succession of decent-chap commanders, out-thought and out-gunned the enemy. With his talk of straight bats and knocking 'em for six, Monty seems to exemplify the victory of Human over Inhuman. Virtue Victorious, Villainy Vanquished.

Then comes the massive and decisive Russian defeat of their Nazi invaders. The tattered, bloody remnants of the 6th German Army surrenders at Stalingrad. Even Nick can understand how epic the struggle must have been: soldiers frozen to their weapons, bloodstained snow and ice, nightmare battles in shattered cities or on frozen rivers, bodies dangling from gibbets, tanks and aircraft that won't start in hellish sub-zero temperatures, burned crops, burned villages, burned cities. Even a great victory – on paper – becomes yet another defeat as the invaders' supply lines stretch endlessly – and snap. Then the awful Russian winter closes in... In Berlin, German women give their fur coats to the war effort. They might as well offer boxes of matches.

We have won the wars of the oceans. The U-boats that threatened to starve us of food, men and munitions are overcome. The little island of Britain is not, after all, cut off from its friends and supporters.

In the air, the Blitz is about-turned. Now it is the Germans who quake in their shelters as USAAF bombers roar overhead in the daytime. In the night, the RAF smashes and firestorms whole cities with thousand-bomber raids. And now, the bombs are many times bigger, and more effective. So are navigation and target-finding techniques. The Blitz of 1940 was a bow-and-arrow affair compared with the

Allied raids of 1943.

We are winning: but when and where does it end? How long will the American-Japanese struggle go on in the Far East and Pacific? Monster US battleships and aircraft carriers are sunk by Jap aircraft. Island battles are fought hand to hand in poisonous jungles. How do you win such straggling, far-flung wars? And when?

Pig-ignorant Nick hasn't a clue. Has anyone else? Would it be of any use to ask the Captains and the Kings, the commanders and overlords?

Or should you instead ask bespectacled men and women in laboratory coats? What would you ask them about? A sort of death ray derived from radar? Nerve gases? Chemical warfare? Remote-controlled, pilotless missiles?

Even something to do with splitting the atom?

Oh, come on now, let's not be fanciful.

Call-up cannot be too far distant. O'Leary, dressed as an OHMS envelope, will call a command that must be obeyed. As his Majesty King George VI is well aware, Nick is nineteen.

He has not changed all that much since leaving school. He does not really want to change. His narrow six-foot frame is a little more experienced in the pains and pleasures of the flesh. His mind and hand, fundamentally unaltered, are becoming stocked with the tools of his trade. He can draw just about well enough for publication; play instruments well enough to survive among professionals; and write prose that occasionally earns money – though, like most beginners, he agonizes far too much over the words he taps out. Everything must be revised, chopped, reassorted, tickled up or toned down. Nothing comes easily.

JIMBO

Nick meets his friend Jimbo, a coffee-coloured West Indian with a relaxed, slender body and a head as neatly shaped as the head of a match. He makes the Anglo-Saxon Nick feel like a rubbish tip. Jimbo is built, Nick is thrown together.

"Hi there, gate, what's your state?" Jimbo says. He has picked up jive talk from American servicemen and Slim Gaillard records. He speaks it with the same easy speed that he plays single-note lines on the guitar. But he is weak on chords; so he and Nick take in each other's washing, playing duets.

"You still play that sad old piece of lumber?" he says, giving Nick's guitar case a little kick. "You want to see what I got with me, boy. You come down here and never fear, you'll shed a tear! Oh yeah, oh yeah!"

They go down the stairs of the little Soho dive, the HobNob. Jimbo has keys for the three padlocks. They enter the low, long, stale cellar. It is afternoon, the place is empty. Jimbo's smile is the only thing clearly seen by the light of the single light bulb. Jimbo dives behind the little bar and drags out a new guitar case covered in mock lizard skin. His cuffs gleam white: he is hot on collars and cuffs, starches them himself.

"All-American carved-top Gibson, feller! Straight from those gates in the States! Ever see such a mellow cello?"

He kisses it tenderly and begins to play and sing.

> *"The king of the cannibal islands*
> *Invited me to tea.*
> *And there at the top of the menu*
> *Was – Me!"*

"You crummy bum," Nick says. "Those chords are horrible." He gets his own guitar out. They play together. Jimbo goes "Whoo! Smooth!" when Nick puts in cunning chord modulations. They are happy.

They stop and drink gin. Nick says, "How the hell did you get that thing?"

"From a Yankee friend, boy. Yankee make it, Jimbo take it. It's a gift for services rendered. Solid render, solid sender!"

"What did you give the Yank for it?"

"Rosalee. You remember her? My side dish."

"You don't mean—"

"I surely do, I tell you true. He gets her ... how long? A week or so and what d'yknow, he's drafted out and it's all vout!"

"What about Rosalee? Does she think everything's vout?"

"You know Rosalee."

"Yes, but—"

"And I know guitars. A *Gibson* man! Look at it and weep! Rosalee, she'll be back. He go, she come. Goodbye laddie, back to Daddy. I speak sooth and that's the truth. Here, grab some!" He hands the guitar to Nick.

Nick runs through some chords. For the first time

in his life, they seem easy to finger. The Gibson's
action is superb. He groans with envy.

"When you go?" Jimbo suddenly asks.

"Go? Oh, you mean call-up. Soon, I suppose. Any
time now."

"That's right, you go soon, boy, you fight Hitler
like I did. You'll just love it, yes you will! I mean,
who needs two feet?"

Jimbo was a Merchant Navy seaman. His left foot
was blown off in 1941. They gave him a tin replace-
ment, his discharge and enough money – it didn't
take much – to open the HobNob.

"Those Nazis," Jimbo says, "you'll come to love
them. Sweet as pie and that's no lie." He takes his
guitar and starts singing to the tune of "Colonel
Bogey".

Hitler
Has only got one ball
Goering's
Are really ra-ther small
Himmler
Is somewhat simmler
And as for Goebbels
He's noebbels
At all.

"Beautiful, that was," Nick says. "There's nothing
like the classics."

Jimbo grins. "You want to go?" he asks.

"Yes, of course. Well, yes."

"Me, I want this Gibson," Jimbo says. He gives
the guitar another kiss.

EROTICAL

Well, do I want to go? Nick asks himself as he trudges along Charlotte Street. A world war and little old me. I wonder how we'll get on together.

He reaches the pub where all the homosexuals used to go and stands outside it, staring vaguely at the closed doors. Pubs won't open for another hour or two.

When was he here? Years ago, he was still a schoolboy. Polly took him – Polly, widow of an actor. She had a high, drifting voice that said outrageous things. She was shameless yet blameless, a shocker whose shocks never stung.

"Oh, Nick! – you must see this, just look!" she'd say, handing him a naughty French magazine whose pictures made his cheeks go pink. "No, not that bit – how do they get them that way? Do you think they use a bicycle pump? – no – here, this little advertisement for dirty books ... *The Twenty-two Positions of Love ... very erotical.* Very erotical, isn't that nice?"

To further his education, she took him to the wicked pub. He opened the door for her, she went in first. Through the door he could hear a tumult of voices, smell scenty smells.

Then he, Nick, the fair-haired all-British teenage dreamboat, entered.

All conversation stopped. Men with ear-rings, men comparing tricky new cigarette lighters, pretty young fellows with shirts open to the waist, dainty old things with frilly cuffs and silver hair swept back in wings – they all stopped talking and gazed at him with speculative eyes.

Ten seconds later the conversations started again, swelling to fill the little pub as water fills a jug.

He got used to the place quite soon. (Polly did not need to: she was at home immediately, anywhere.) He drank beer, filled his pipe but decided not to light it. It was not a place for pipemen.

A smooth, pink, elderly man with blue-rinsed white hair had been giving Nick sidelong looks. At last the man addressed him, directly, staring blearily with mascara eyes.

"Yes, *well*, one can see at a *glance*, can't one?" he accused.

"See what?"

"That you don't approve of us! Oh, don't deny, one always knows. A *disapproving* one, yes you are, one can always tell."

Nick mumbled and attended to his beer.

"Well, let me tell you one little thing, my young friend – some of us served King and Country in the *last* war! One was proud to serve!"

"You were in the forces?"

"A *soldier*, your genuine Tommy Atkins! Khaki! And in the *trenches*, quite horrible, but one was *there*, facing the Boche!"

"So you saw plenty of action?" Nick asks, burying his face in his glass.

"Well, not precisely *action*. But we were terribly *determined*. And let me tell you one thing, young man: our trenches were the tidiest in the whole of France."

Nick gazes at the closed pub, still asking himself "Do you want to go?"

A lot depends on which service. Navy, no. Sea-sickness. Army, definitely not – he'd never be able to keep his trench tidy, ha ha. That man in the pub must have been sending me up. Or himself.

But the RAF ... flying ... well, that's different. He has seen, liked and admired the RAF. But would the RAF return the compliment?

He strolls on. A gig this evening, a train to Sussex tomorrow. But right now, a movie. What's on here? War film, don't want war films. Ah, a Hollywood musical. Escape.

Nick walks from the station to the small grey house, the new family home. His mother is cheerful. Her daughter has got leave, she is coming home for two whole days! But she is bringing her Norwegian boyfriend, it all sounds *most* mysterious, and how will the rations stretch?

"A Norwegian?" Nick says.

"Yes, a Norwegian. I have been to Denmark, I know a number of Danes. But *Norwegians*... Apparently his name is Storm. *Storm*..." She shudders slightly.

Bloody hell, Nick thinks, I can just see him. Six foot three, icy blue eyes, sun tan, broad shoulders and a heroic past: one of those Scandinavians who faced impossible odds and rowed all the way here, fighting off Stukas and U-boats with home-made catapults. Don't want to meet him, can't face it.

He does not have to.

"Oh, and there's a letter for you," his mother tells him. "On the hall table. OHMS. I think you'd better open it immediately."

He opens it. It contains his call-up papers.

My God, it's happened.

Thank heaven, it's the RAF.

LATE NIGHT FINALE

Nick spends his last night of freedom looking for a girl calling herself Leslie de Paris. She lives with her parents in south London. The name on the door of their flat is Lefkowicz.

Leslie should be at the Riffs, singing in front of a five-piece band. The man guarding the door says, "Leslie? You want Leslie? You and Mr Sammy both." Mr Sammy is the dark-suited, neckless, swarthy owner of the club. "*He* wanted Leslie, want her bad. And see what he got!"

He jerks his head at an explosive stain on the wall. "She throw things, chairs, bottles, things like that," he tells Nick. "He try it on, she brush him off."

"Where can I find her?"

The man doesn't bother to answer. Nick reverses his guitar case in the narrow entrance and leaves, scowling. He has reason. Leslie is gorgeous. She has velvety cream-olive skin, daring eyes and dark, vigorous hair that looks as if Brylcreemed but isn't: some inner lusciousness from her rounded body must seep through her scalp.

Tomorrow Nick is to be enlisted as a Brylcreem boy – an RAF man. He *must* find Leslie, he *must* end his civilian life with an exclamation mark. She's got to be singing somewhere – but in which of perhaps ten clubs?

He finds her, much later, at the Tin Tac.

Although she is in the middle of "Lover Man", just about the most difficult number any chantoozie can attempt, she directs a quarter of a smile at him. His heart jumps for joy and his mind begins planning.

Where will she change? Over there, behind those dingy double curtains, where they stack tonic water and all the rest of it. She will bang her creamy elbows against crates of empties, make up her face frowning into the usual rusty mirror, sniff her gently curved, un-English nose at the stink of damp carpet, mice, cat's pee, flattened fag ends and left over sweat. The glamour of showbiz.

After "Lover Man" they'll do something up-tempo and she will finish her set. He listens to her. She can't hold the last long note, instead she has to wag her head and make her lips tremble with deep emotion. Nobody notices, some people clap. Nick claps like mad. He moves closer to the double curtains. Soon he will "help" her to change...

She is finished, she is moving towards him, automatically fending off hands reaching for her satin-clad bottom, saying, "Why, *thank* you, thank you so *much*!" to anyone whose lips move, steering a course that keeps her well away from a table full of drunks.

"Oh, Nick! Oh, good, someone nice at last! I'll start changing, you come in when that dancer comes on, they'll all be looking at her." The curtains swish and he hears her sneeze from their dust.

Minutes later he is crammed in with her and the empties, repeating the line that first won her. "Oh, that *back*!" he says, caressing it with a fingertip. "The most beautiful back in the world!" And she, bless her, makes the same reply as she did the first time: "Nobody's ever said that to me before," she breathes. "Have I really got such a nice back?"

He carefully keeps his eyes from her sumptuous front, encased in a lightly soiled bra. Her *back*, remember, it's her *back*. She puts on street clothes and hands him the little case containing her show stuff. "Do you want to take me home?" she says.

He does, very much.

They even find a taxi. It is a long drive to the flat in south London. They manage to make the time fly.

Then comes a nasty shock: it is the family flat, the family is there! Mr Lefkowicz with his cigar, Mrs Lefkowicz with her rings and smiles and bulging handbag, even an elder sister Lefkowicz with fabric samples on her lap and all over the floor. But – "Is that the time already? Am I mad? Fly, I must fly!" – and she is away.

One Lefkowicz gone but two to go. Not a hope.

He has failed to recognize that the Lefkowiczs are Gents. There are two classes of people in the world: Gents and non-Gents. Gents, irrespective of race, age or sex, are people who don't do wrong things, because that might cause someone hurt. Much more importantly, their instincts make them do *right* things.

So Mr Lefkowicz rises from his chair, makes a great show of yawning and stretching, and says, "Time to turn in". And Mrs Lefkowicz makes everything clear by adding, "We should leave the young ones alone, yes? And so goodnight, goodnight, lock up safe and sound, so nice meeting you, mister err-err."

The family exchanges smiles, pats and kisses. Leslie says, "Mama, I will take a bath. I won't disturb you?"

"A bath, food, tea, anything."

The bath is in one corner of the living room, hidden by a check curtain. Leslie is already undressing.

Nick says, "You must have the nicest parents in the world."

"Their daughter is nice, too," she says, throwing aside her last scrap of clothing. "Very nice, don't you think?" She raises her arms and slowly turns round, displaying herself.

"You can use the bath after me," she says, settling back in the scented water. She soaps herself. She looks so lovely that Nick finds himself gulping and misty-eyed. Perhaps he and Leslie have drunk too much of the various drinks from the jazzy Lefkowicz cocktail cabinet.

GET FELL IN

Next day, Nick is gulping and bleary-eyed at Lord's Cricket ground. It is a stifling day in late summer, 1943. He is no longer intimately alone with a sweet-smelling and lovely female but one among a thousand or so sweat-soaked young men.

He is at Lords not to play cricket but to be inducted into the Royal Air Force.

He has a suitcase and a blinding hangover headache. He stands for what seems hours in the sun while somebody somewhere shouts incomprehensible instructions through a PA system, then is marched, with thirty or forty others, to a nearby garage where he is kitted out. Clothes that don't fit are thrown at him; then a canvas tube, a kit bag, into which the clothes won't fit.

An RAF corporal, a mottled old sweat, awaits them

outside a little shop near the garage. "Stand straight, you doz-y shower!" he bellows. "Right – fall out five at a time. Metal polish and blanco. You buy them here. With your own money. First five – you lot – get in there, at the double."

A cocky new boy grins and says, "No can do, Corp. No money."

"Borrow some from a mate."

"Got no mates, Corp." His grin becomes cockier and more challenging.

The corporal stares, the recruit stares back.

The corporal says, "You've got a friend in me, sonny." He comes closer and grinds his right fist into his left palm. "You're just my sort, son," he says. "I eat two of you before breakfast."

The recruit breaks. He draws back, mumbles and accepts coins from someone standing near him.

"Right, now get in there!" the corporal bellows. "AT THE DOUBLE!"

Nick wonders what rake-off he gets from the shopkeeper.

Humping their kitbags, webbing and suitcases, the new lot is marched along the road to a block of flats by the Regent's Park canal. "Up them stairs!" a corporal shouts. "Grab your pits!" They scramble up the stairs and fling equipment on bunks to bag a bed space.

These were luxury flats. They are no longer luxurious. The windows have been nearly filled in with bricks against bomb blast. One brick is omitted against suffocation. There are six or eight people to each small room.

"Bloody civvy jail's better nor this!" someone grumbles.

"How would you know? You been in jail?"

"Too right, chum."

Nick has been unlucky. Everyone but he in his cell is a Scot. They gibber and yell in Celtic. Nick can understand only one word they say, the F word. "Heuch the wurra!" they shout at him. "D'ye nae ken the fleuther glimroc beddie's hecht fer ooo'r wee Jimmie?" They try to push him from the bed he has bagged.

"Awa' wi ye!" they shout. "Och, unco pewkie yarreuh, wha' boot ooo'r Jimmie?"

"Who the hell's this Jimmie?" Nick says, grabbing his kit bag back as soon as it is snatched from him.

"D'ye nae ken ooo'r Jimmie?" They stare at Nick, amazed. "Hoots, mon! Ooo' Jimmie's *Scotland's Fred Astaire!*"

Jimmie does not look much like Fred Astaire. He shuffles his feet, dancing. The Scots make reverential noises. Nick scowls and won't give up his bed. On it, he lays out his new possessions.

Slate-blue shirts with separate collars and front and backbone studs. A brass button stick. A "hussif" – housewife – a cloth roll containing needles, thread, buttons and so on. Black gym plimsolls. Lots of canvas webbing items. Service gas mask to replace his civilian one. Thick-soled black boots. Uniform. Kit bag, to be marked with his name and seven-figure service number, a number he knows he will never forget.

Nick packs his own clothes in the brown paper

provided and ties it with coarse string, also provided. He fills in the label provided. His and hundreds of identical parcels will be delivered home.

Home...

"I'm back in prison," he says to himself. Boarding school was prison: you escaped. But now you're back. And this time, there's no remission, no school-holiday paroles.

He fills in the label with his fountain pen, unaware that he is using it for the last time. In the night, someone "liberates" it.

Early next morning, they are marched across the road to what was the Zoo's Tea Rooms. Corporals swear at them, the zoo gibbons greet them with their lost-souls' morning chorus of hoots and wails. For the first time, Nick uses his Issue irons – knife, fork and spoon.

There is grey porridge and strange-tasting tea. "That's the bleeding bromide," someone tells him. "Bromide, see? Supposed to stop you getting randy."

The bromide doesn't work. Every evening, the banks of the canal are littered with new airmen and young and old females. The grass is flattened, the canal waters filled with bobbing souvenirs of passion.

Nick is fortunate. He has somewhere to go, people to visit. He only has to buy a tube ticket. But now all his old friends seem like foreigners – glorious and remote members of an alien tribe that drinks tea not dosed with bromide. They are not shouted at, herded, numbered. They even wear their own clothes.

Gym in the park. Hundreds of erks – lowest RAF life-form – jump up and down in ill-fitting long shorts, or chase each other in a ring following instructions to hit the bottom of the man in front with their plimsolls.

Nick is questioned, jabbed with hypodermics, inspected, marched, screamed at, drilled, moved from here to there "AT THE DOUBLE!" At first his mind is black with resentment. Quite soon, he sees the light: he has been caught in a grinding machine. The machine is too enormous to care about him personally, it is programmed only to grind anyone, everyone. So it grinds.

The machine can be fooled now and then. In another block of ravaged flats, he is examined as to his suitability to be an aircrew cadet.

"And what were your sports at school?" a young officer asks. Nick can tell that this is an important question. "Well, sir, first eleven cricket and soccer of course," he lies.

"*Soccer?* You mean, your school didn't go in for *rugger?*" the officer says, his face clouded with horrid doubts.

"Oh, gosh yes, sir! Bags of it! And I was ... rather keen, actually."

"Good show. Well, in that case..."

The officer, relieved, loses interest. He has hundreds more recruits to deal with and most, by the look of them, wouldn't know silly mid-off from scrum-half (nor would Nick).

Nick enters bright rooms where a sort of cattle show goes on. Half naked, he is made to gape, cough, bend over, and say ninety-nine.

He enters dark rooms where he is chained by the

neck to his chair in front of a round table where
other erks, similarly chained to prevent them leaning forward, peer at a dimly lit display of little
silhouettes — bus, aeroplane, ship and so on. This
test is for night vision. Nick does so well at it that
he is made to take the test a second time.

Then calamity. Another dark room is arranged as
a black tunnel. At the far end, tiny electric bulbs
glimmer, one after another. The colour-vision test.
"Red," says the erk in front. Then, "Green …
yellow."

To the colour-blind Nick, the coloured lights are
just spots of brightness. "Cripes!" he says to the
person standing behind him, "help me out!"

"What's it worth?"

"Packet of five."

"Make it ten." Nick nods. The lights go on and
off. "Red," mutters his accomplice. "Red!" says
Nick, loud and clear. "Yellow … white…"

Nick has passed. He hands over two five-packets
of Players Weights. There has never been time, since
joining up, to fill and smoke his pipe.

"Squint," says a nice-looking WAAF junior officer.
Another failure looms: Nick can't squint. Most of
his childhood friends could and did. A boy called
Fernandez could not only squint his great brown
eyes, he could make his eyes go completely white.

"Can't squint?" says the WAAF officer. She laughs.
"Look at this pencil. Keep looking." She moves the
pencil nearer and nearer Nick's eyes. "There!" she
says, laughing again. "You squinted!"

Hers is the only pleasing Service voice he has
heard since that first day at Lord's Cricket Ground.

TOTAL SURRENDER

The grinding machine swallows ninety-five per cent of Nick.

He is selected for Air Crew training. Good, very good!

He gets fell in and is called a horrible little man, a dozy lot, a ... one-man disaster. Not so good.

In Torquay, he is drilled on the promenade by a corporal who tells him to slam down his heel coming to attention – "I WANT THEM HEELS TO CRACK THAT CONCRETE!"

Nick suffers agonies from drill because his new boots scrape the skin off his heels and toes. Yet he more than half enjoys his agony. "Old Corp!" someone says, unwillingly admiring, "he should have been an actor!" Well, he is. The concrete-cracking corporal can give his head a backward flip that throws his forage cap over his right shoulder: then catch it as it falls without looking.

And the PTIs, physical-training NCOs, they are actors too. They take squads of erks for crucifying runs that shatter even the hard lads who've done it all – make them sob and slaver, knees buckling. But the PTIs shout, "Come on, you fairies! Let's have you – all be fairies!" They leap in mid-stride, do balletic bits with their arms, kick bottoms, burst into song. Then they take out another squad and do it all over again.

Nick learns to fall off the tailgate of a moving lorry; to dive over a line of chairs; to darn his socks, make up his bed-pack so that it resembles a geometrical poem; to name friendly and enemy aircraft from silhouettes; to work navigational computers and plot courses; to strip down and reassemble Browning machine guns; to live a communal life; to polish brass and blanco webbing; and, very important, to use a bone, spittle and Cherry Blossom polish to turn the toes of his boots into convex mirrors.

The bullshit takes more time than the instruction on matters to do with becoming an Air Crew member. Nick has never been near a kite. He knows nothing of aircraft engines, cockpit layouts, armament and a million other things.

These may come later. Meanwhile, caught in the jaws of the machine, he is resigned to pig ignorance. Only five per cent of his own being remains, in the form of bent and frayed books stuck in his kit bag, some old photographs, some new friends.

Pig ignorant. But like it or not, he is learning.

ORDINARY SEAMAN

John Gordon

Towards the end of the Second World War, the teenage John Gordon served as an Ordinary Seaman on board a minesweeper. He had some harrowing experiences; coming to terms with the peculiar traditions, practices and language of the Navy was a trial in itself... This fascinating memoir is his story.

SMOKESTACK LIGHTNING

Laurence Staig

The son of a showman, Laurence Staig grew up among circus performers and fairground folk. His greatest love, though, was for rhythm and blues – the music of the Rolling Stones and Howlin' Wolf, singer of the soulful "Smokestack Lightning". The Sixties were coming to life and Laurence was determined to be in on the action.

"An entertaining memoir... Written so that we can share the exuberance of youth, rather than see it from the point of view of an adult reflecting on his past."
Sian Dronfield (15), The Independent on Sunday

YESTERDAY

Adèle Geras

When, as a teenager, Adèle Geras visited Oxford for the first time, she fell in love with it at once. She went up to the university in 1963, the year President Kennedy was assassinated and the Beatles released their first LP. Joining the theatre crowd, she soon found herself involved in dramas on and off the stage. This entertaining "Sixties" memoir is her story.

THE BURNING BABY
AND OTHER GHOSTS

John Gordon

The glowing ashes turned again and then, from the centre, there arose a small entity, a little shape of fire. It had a small torso, small limbs, and a head of flame. And it walked.

A teenage girl disappears mysteriously a few days before bonfire night; two youths out skating see something grisly beneath the ice; an elderly spinster feeds her young charge to the eels… Unnatural or violent death are at the heart of these five supernatural tales, in which wronged spirits seek to exact a terrible and terrifying retribution on the living. Vivid as fire, chilling as ice, their stories will haunt you.

"All the stories include hauntingly memorable apparitions… A major collection." *Ramsey Campbell, Necrofile*

THE DARK CARD

Amy Ehrlich

*On the night table were a pile of chips,
a few bills and some other jewellery...
And there was also a gun...*

Alone in the family house near Atlantic City,
Laura is struggling to come to terms with her
mother's recent death when she meets Billy, a
blackjack dealer in one of the casinos on A.C.'s
infamous Boardwalk. Soon she finds herself
drawn into the flashy, alluring, high-risk world
of the gambling tables, where the dark card is
queen and nothing is as it seems.

"Extremely carefully crafted and a compulsive
read." *School Librarian*

THE FLITHER PICKERS

Theresa Tomlinson

"Northern sea, silver sea,
Bring my daddy home to me,
Hush the waves and still the sea,
And bring my daddy back to me."

Life is hard for the fisher folk living and working on the north-east coast at the turn of the century. The men face death daily in the often stormy sea, while the women, the flither pickers, gather bait from the shore. Children who are too young to work, like Liza Welford, are supposed to go to school. But what have books and sums to do with a child of the sea?

Based on real events, this novel is illustrated with black-and-white photographs of the period by the celebrated Frank Meadow Sutcliffe.

"A gritty, touching novel of the North Yorkshire coast." *The Guardian*

CALABRIAN QUEST

Geoffrey Trease

Her heart nearly stopped... The figure was human – but the head upturned to meet her incredulous stare was the head of a wolf.

A fifth-century Roman christening spoon is the catalyst for this thrilling adventure which sees Max, a young American, travel to Italy with Andy, Karen and her cousin Julie on a quest for lost treasure. It's not long, though, before they encounter some sinister happenings and find themselves in conflict with the local Mafia...

"A gripping story of archaeological adventure... The tale rattles along, demonstrating an unputdownability as durable as [Geoffrey Trease] himself."
Mary Hoffman, The Sunday Telegraph

"From storytelling such as this, readers are infected with a love of books."
Jill Paton Walsh,
The Times Educational Supplement

WHY WEEPS THE BROGAN?

Hugh Scott

WED. 4 YEARS 81 DAYS FROM HOSTILITIES ... so reads the date on the clock in central hall.
For Saxon and Gilbert, though, it's just another day in their ritualized indoor existence. Saxon bakes, Gilbert brushes, together they visit the Irradiated Food Store, guarding against spiders. Among the dusty display cases, however, a far more disturbing creature moves...
But what is the Brogan? And why does it weep?

"Deftly evoked, the narrative is cleverly constructed, and there is no denying the nightmarish power of the story. There is a true shock ending."
The Listener

"A very compelling and very interesting book."
Jill Paton Walsh
The Times Educational Supplement

A Whitbread Novel Award Winner
Shortlisted for the McVitie's Prize

BACKTRACK

Peter Hunt

"Our Correspondent in Hereford last night informed us of another shocking railway catastrophe. A train was derailed near the village of Elmcote with terrible results..." The Times, Friday, September 3rd, 1915

When Jack and Rill meet one summer, they discover that they both had great uncles involved in an old and still unexplained railway crash. So who better to try to find out what really happened?

"A smashing mystery/thriller... If you like ideas as well as action, *Backtrack* is for you."
Weekend

"Imaginative ... a nice astringent variant on the boy-girl motif."
The Observer

MORE WALKER PAPERBACKS
For You to Enjoy

☐ 0-7445-2378-8   *Ordinary Seaman*
                     by John Gordon   £2.99

☐ 0-7445-2379-6   *Smokestack Lightning*
                     by Laurence Staig   £2.99

☐ 0-7445-2352-4   *Yesterday*
                     by Adèle Geras   £2.99

☐ 0-7445-3080-6   *The Burning Baby*
                     and Other Ghosts
                     by John Gordon   £2.99

☐ 0-7445-3021-0   *The Dark Card*
                     by Amy Ehrlich   £2.99

☐ 0-7445-2043-6   *The Flither Pickers*
                     by Theresa Tomlinson   £3.99

☐ 0-7445-2304-4   *Calabrian Quest*
                     by Geoffrey Trease   £2.99

☐ 0-7445-2040-1   *Why Weeps the Brogan?*
                     by Hugh Scott   £2.99

☐ 0-7445-1466-5   *Backtrack*
                     by Peter Hunt   £3.99